TRENCHERMAN'S
GUIDE

Trencherman's Guide is
supported by

SALCOMBE
GIN

Salt Media, 5 Cross Street, Devon, EX31 1BA.
www.saltmedia.co.uk
Tel: 01271 859299
Email: ideas@saltmedia.co.uk

Written, designed and produced by
Nick Cooper, Sophie Chamier, Catherine Courtenay, Lucy Deasy, Claire Fegan, Kathryn Lewis, Abi Manning, Tamsin Powell, Jo Rees, Rosanna Rothery, Christopher Sheppard, Katie Taylor and Linda Weller.

Big salute to South West photographers Guy Harrop and David Griffen who created many of the stunning images in this year's guide.

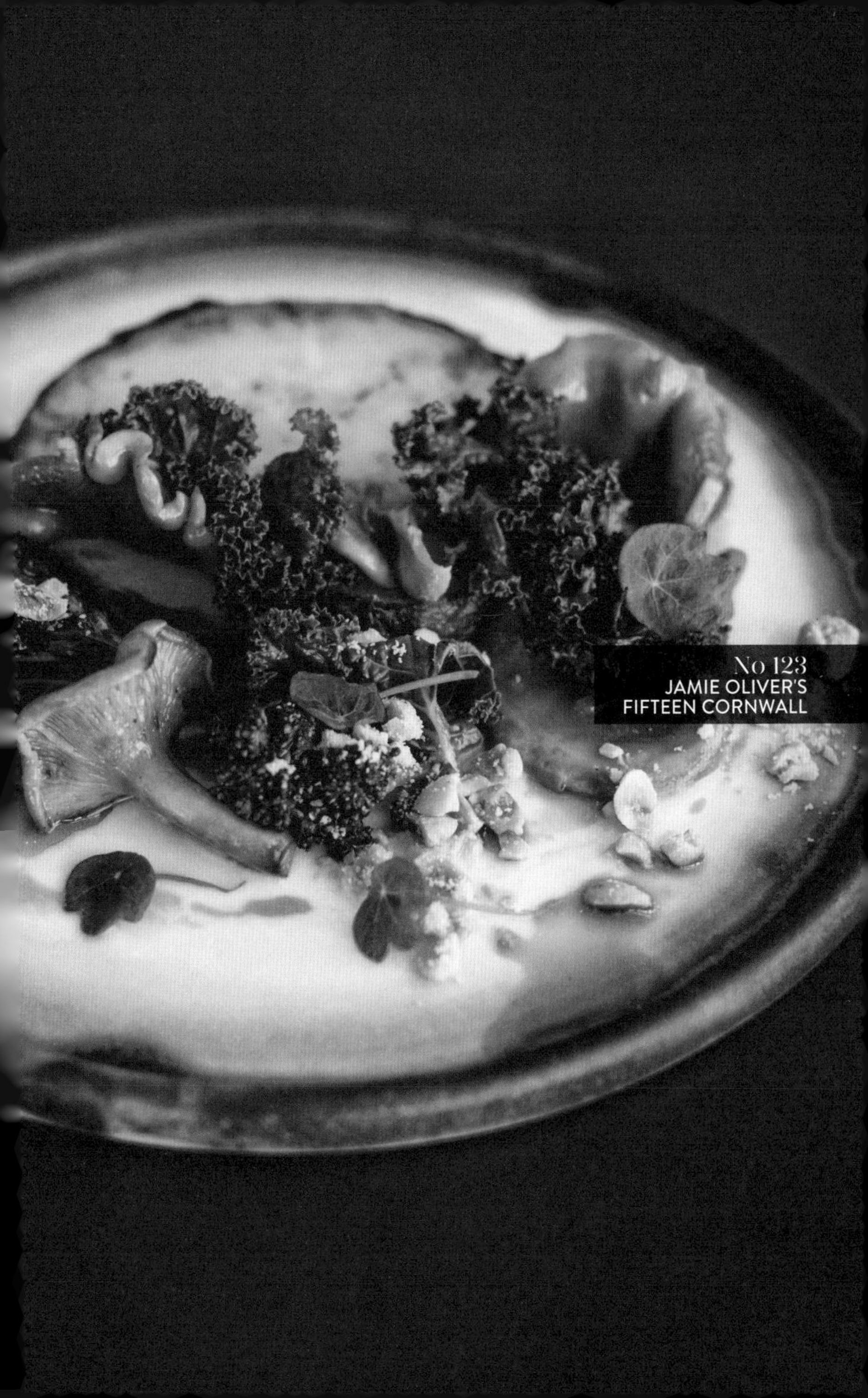

No 123
JAMIE OLIVER'S
FIFTEEN CORNWALL

Foreword

'The South West's original guide to exceptional dining continues to flourish'

It's wonderful to see an even greater number of establishments in this year's edition – including many restaurants which haven't graced our pages before.

The South West's original guide to exceptional dining continues to flourish. In addition to new discoveries in the guide, you can also find special events and offers from member restaurants in our fortnightly email from Trencherman's HQ.

If you're not a member of the Trencherman's Club yet, do sign up (it's free) as it's a treasure trove of exclusive must-dos. See details on page 14.

Each year we aim to make the guide more gorgeous and user friendly, so I hope you enjoy flicking through the 26th edition and earmarking some of the region's most fabulous restaurants to visit.

On behalf of the member restaurants, our chairman Michael Caines MBE, the Trencherman's committee and the team at Salt Media who carefully compile the guide each year, thank you for being part of the journey.

Here's to another year of astoundingly good dining.

Jo Rees
Editor

contents

No 23
THE BUNCH OF GRAPES

Welcome

'We're proud to represent the very best dining in the South West and continue the Trencherman's tradition'

Last year we celebrated the Trencherman's Guide's quarter century birthday and this year we're excited to produce an even larger guide, which bodes well for the future of restaurants in our region.

However, at a time when our high streets increasingly look like copycats of each other, it's more important than ever to celebrate the authentic and independent.

All of the Trencherman's restaurants are independently owned, often by chef patrons like myself who have made it their life's mission to create exceptional dining experiences.

We know that the readers of the Trencherman's Guide appreciate the unprecedented detail and care that goes into cooking and serving food at this level, and it's our pleasure to share our passion with you.

As a group of chefs we are proud to represent the best dining in the South West and continue the Trencherman's tradition. After all, the guide was started by chefs and hoteliers with the aim of guiding gourmets to the kind of special establishments that we'd like to visit.

Member restaurants are only invited to be in the guide on the basis of achieving consistently high ratings across a selection of top international publications (including *The Michelin Guide*, *The Good Food Guide* and the *AA Restaurant Guide*), so you're in safe hands.

Salut!

Michael Caines MBE
Chairman of the Trencherman's committee

join the club

The Trencherman's Club is the way to find out about the guide's exclusive offers and events

It's free and you'll receive the information in a fortnightly e-newsletter. Naturally, we won't share your details.

Sign up now at

trenchermans-guide.com

Join the conversation

f The Trenchermans Guide

𝕏 @trenchermans

Left: Pork loin, cheek, kimchi, broccoli and sesame dish – created by Alex Betts of The Chequers (No 31) for the 2018 Trencherman's Awards dinner

2018

TRENCHERMAN'S

AWARDS

Cooking at the 2018 Trencherman's Awards were (left-right):
Jamie Gulliford of Salcombe Harbour Hotel (No 108), Alex Betts
of The Chequers (No 31), Stephane Delourme of The Seafood Restaurant
(No 118) and Jude Kereama of Kota Restaurant with Rooms (No 134)

The South West's finest chefs, hoteliers and industry insiders come together each November to discover who has won the Trencherman's Awards

Trencherman's readers vote in their thousands to crown their favourite restaurants, dining pubs, chefs and more. The 2018 award winners were revealed at a glamorous dinner at Salcombe Harbour Hotel where the 2017 winners each cooked a stunning course.

Here's who took the top honours – find them in the guide ...

BEST RESTAURANT
The Idle Rocks
No 128

BEST DINING PUB
The Swan
No 68

BEST CHEF
Michael Wignall,
Gidleigh Park
No 78

BEST FRONT OF HOUSE TEAM
Lewtrenchard Manor
No 92

BEST DINE AND STAY EXPERIENCE
Glazebrook House Hotel
No 85

BEST BAR LIST
The Pump House
No 27

AWARD FOR CREATIVITY AND INNOVATION
Lympstone Manor
No 73

using the guide

The guide is divided into regions, with higher members (who reach a higher level in the strict Trencherman's scoring) having an image and longer description than other members.

Each entry is numbered and included on the map at the start of each region.

Look for the following symbols at the top of each restaurant for additional information.

All Trencherman's restaurants meet a strict scoring criteria to be included, so you can be confident that they offer an exceptional experience.

TRENCHERMAN'S AWARDS FINALISTS

Trencherman's members who won a 2018 Trencherman's Award are celebrated throughout the guide with a full page which tells you more about them. You can also identify the finalists by looking for this symbol.

SPECIAL PLACES TO STAY

To find Trencherman's restaurants with rooms and foodie hotels, look out for this symbol.

Left: Grilled whole red mullet, crab, chilli and basil – created by Stephane Delourme of The Seafood Restaurant (No 118) for the 2018 Trencherman's Awards dinner

Gloucestershire

Gloucestershire

Restaurants listed in the guide correspond to the numbers plotted on the map.

■ Higher member | ▦ Member

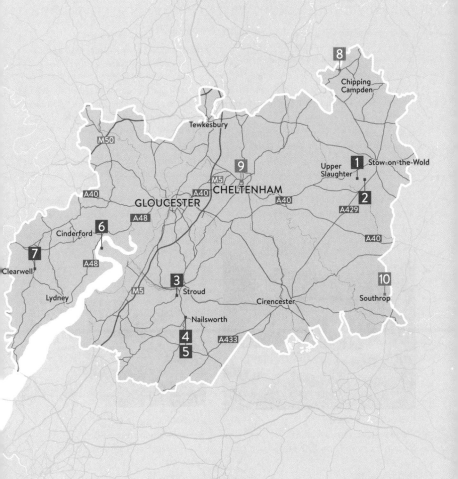

Tewkesbury

M50

A40

GLOUCESTER

A48

Cinderford

Clearwell

Lydney

M5

A48

Stroud

Nailsworth

A433

M5

A40

CHELTENHAM

A40

Upper
Slaughter

Stow-on-the-Wold

A429

A40

Cirencester

Southrop

1

2

3

4

5

6

7

8

9

10

Chipping
Campden

LORDS OF THE MANOR HOTEL

Classic country hideaway

In the heart of the Cotswolds, this 17th century manor house hotel is tucked away in eight acres of beautifully landscaped gardens.

The 26 ensuite bedrooms feature elegantly luxurious country-style decor – and you can hire the whole hotel exclusively if you're planning a wedding or party with wow factor.

Enjoy accomplished modern British/European fine dining in the restaurant with views of the walled garden. Chef Charles Smith has some top UK restaurants on his CV and his guiding principle is to source the best (though not necessarily local) ingredients. Pair your plate with a pick from the house sommelier's impressive collection.

Chef **Charles Smith**
3 course lunch from **£28.50**
3 course dinner from **£72.50**
Seats **46**
Bedrooms **26**
Room rate from **£195**

Upper Slaughter, near Bourton-on-the-Water, Gloucestershire, GL54 2JD
01451 820243

www.lordsofthemanor.com

f Lords of the Manor Hotel
🐦 @cotswoldlords
📷 @lordsofthemanor

THE SLAUGHTERS MANOR HOUSE

Gorgeous gastronomic getaway

The Slaughters Manor House is a beautiful 17th century hotel with country charm in spades. A winning combination of luxuriously contemporary interiors, excellent service and one of the most highly regarded restaurants in Gloucestershire make it a must-visit for gastronomes in search of glamour.

The award winning brigade, led by Nik Chappell, craft flavour-infused menus from freshly foraged ingredients and top-notch regional produce. And whether you're tucking into Cotswold venison or Cornish crab, the sommelier's wine selections will ensure the experience is sublimely special.

Chef **Nik Chappell**
3 course lunch from **£30**
3 course dinner from **£67.50**
Seats **40**
Bedrooms **19**
Room rate from **£195**

Copsehill Road, Lower Slaughter, Gloucestershire, GL54 2HP
01451 820456

www.slaughtersmanor.co.uk

f The Slaughters Manor House
🐦 @slaughtersmanor
📷 @brownswordhotels

THE BELL AT SELSLEY
Country pub comfort

As much as possible is made in house at this Cotswolds country inn. From ice cream and bread to the mayonnaise and tartare sauce accompanying triple cooked chips and beer battered fish, chef patron Mark Payne crafts it all.

The menu features pub classics as well as dishes such as roasted smoked haddock and slow cooked beef blade. And to accompany the assured cooking, Mark's wife and business partner Sarah Watts ensures guests are well watered – there are over 80 gins and a fine selection of regional ales. We'd recommend ending the evening in one of the oak-beamed guest rooms.

Chef **Mark Payne**
3 course lunch from **£29**
3 course dinner from **£29**
Seats **58**
Bedrooms **2**
Room rate from **£75**

Bell Lane, Selsley, Gloucestershire, GL5 5JY
01453 753801

www.thebellinnselsley.com

f Bell Inn Selsley
🐦 @bellinnselsley
📷 @bellinnselsley

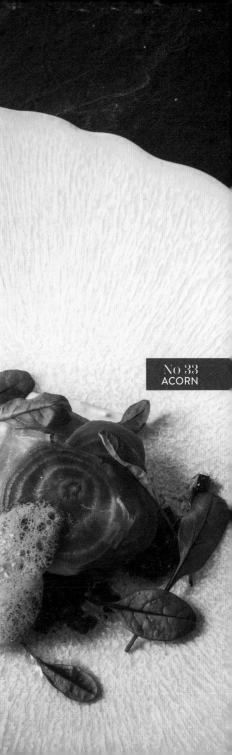

No 33
ACORN

4 S

WILD GARLIC
Stylish restaurant with rooms

When chef Matthew Beardshall moved his award winning tasting menus to his new venture across the road in 2016, Wild Garlic shed its fine dining facade for more relaxed bistro eating.

The family-run restaurant is a hub of good cooking in the busy Cotswolds town of Nailsworth, and popular for its smart lunches, sociable suppers and lazy weekend brunches. Choose from vibrant seasonal salads, house favourites such as aubergine parmigiana or comforting artisan pasta dishes which are handmade each morning by Matthew and newly appointed head chef Joe Francis. Turn a trip into a greedy tour and book one of the five bedrooms and a table at sister restaurant, Wilder.

Chef **Matthew Beardshall**
3 course lunch from **£29**
3 course dinner from **£29**
Seats **44**
Bedrooms **5**
Room rate from **£80**

3 Cossack Square, Nailsworth,
Gloucestershire, GL6 0DB
01453 832615
www.wild-garlic.co.uk

f Wild Garlic Bistro & Rooms
🐦 @thewildgarlic
📷 @wildgarlicnailsworth

5 A

WILDER
Occasion dining in the Cotswolds

The ambitious little sister to Nailsworth stalwart Wild Garlic, Wilder continues to beguile visitors in its second year.

The innovative tasting menus that earned chef patron Matthew Beardshall multiple gongs at Wild Garlic are stepped up a level at this intimate evening dining den. Eight seasonal courses – on a line-up that changes daily – are revealed to diners as each dish reaches the pristine linen-clothed table.

Restaurant manager Faye Wolley provides exquisite wine pairings, while five charming bedrooms above Wild Garlic offer sweet slumber after a suitably memorable meal.

Chef **Matthew Beardshall**
3 course dinner from **£70**
Seats **22**

Market Street, Nailsworth,
Gloucestershire, GL6 0BX
01453 835483
www.dinewilder.co.uk

f Wilder
🐦 @dinewilder
📷 @dinewilder

Old school glamour

29 The Bath Priory

Objet d'art, fine paintings, flower-filled gardens and head chef Michael Nizzero's elegant dishes provide glamorous dressing at this handsome boutique hotel.

126 The Nare Hotel

The beachside hotel that feels like a private house party. Glamour comes in the form of aperitifs at Ken's bar, dining in the yachty Quarterdeck restaurant, sumptuous bedrooms and the hotel's elegant motor launch.

87 Boringdon Hall

Play lord or lady of the manor at this historic country house just outside Plymouth. Head chef Scott Paton's cooking is superb – desserts and pastries especially – and a luxurious in-house spa takes the delight to delirious heights.

2 The Slaughters Manor House

Lavish furnishings, elegant style, flawless service and beautiful food infuse this historic 17th century manor house, bringing it magnificently into the 21st century.

45 The Castle at Taunton

The wisteria-clad Castle is an elegant jewel in Somerset's county town. Head to its Castle Bow restaurant for exquisite cooking in smartly glamorous surroundings.

THE OLD PASSAGE
Seafood by the Severn

Famed for both its seafood and views, The Old Passage should be on every diner's hit list. On the banks of the River Severn and overlooking its lowest crossing point, this is a beautiful spot for dining – indoors or alfresco – with views across the water to the hills of the Forest of Dean.

With seafood the star of the show, the menus change according to what's available. Chef Jon Lane uses ingredients to beautifully enhance the star of each dish, such as the horseradish, shiso and pickled grapes which support the confit Chalk Stream trout.

Highlights include fresh lobster and oysters (from the restaurant's saltwater tanks) and the fabulous fruits de mer.

Chef **Jon Lane**
3 course lunch from **£22.50**
3 course dinner from **£45**
Seats **40**
Bedrooms **2**
Room rate from **£120**

Passage Road, Arlingham,
Gloucestershire, GL2 7JR
01452 740547
www.theoldpassage.com

f The Old Passage
🐦 @oldpassageinn
📷 @the_old_passage

THE MINERS, SLING
Hearty country cooking

As the menu proudly boasts, nearly all of the produce that lands in The Miners' kitchen is sourced within 40 miles of the inn. Chef patron Steven Jenkins puts the impeccably fresh fare to good use, crafting two AA rosette and Taste of the West gold-awarded dishes such as Madgetts duck breast with pumpkin puree and cider potato, and aged Cotswold beef burger with tomato jam, Wookey Hole cheddar and lazy fries (you'll have to visit to find out).

The spacious dining room, with its original bare-brick walls, oak beams and flagstone floors, is relaxed and cosy. There are also a couple of characterful bedrooms and the promise of a full Gloucestershire breakfast the next morning.

Chef **Steven Jenkins**
3 course lunch from **£15.95**
3 course dinner from **£15.95**
Seats **80**
Bedrooms **4**
Room rate from **£80**

Chepstow Road, Sling, Coleford,
Gloucestershire, GL16 8LH
01594 836632
www.theminerssling.co.uk

f The Miners Sling
🐦 @theminerssling

More Gloucestershire

8 S
THE SEAGRAVE ARMS

It would be rude not to start a meal with a Cotswolds Distillery G&T at The Seagrave Arms – after all, the artisan spirit is distilled and bottled just 20 minutes down the road. Sourcing from award winning local suppliers is at the heart of this charming Cotswolds inn, and its countryside location – a short drive from Cheltenham and Stratford-upon-Avon – means there are plenty on its doorstep. Head chef Iain Hobbs crafts the Gloucestershire bounty into crowd-pleasing dishes which he describes as '*upmarket British comfort food*'.

Chef **Iain Hobbs**. 3 course lunch from **£19.95**. 3 course dinner from **£35**. Seats **30**. Bedrooms **8** (plus 2 bed cottage). Room rate from **£100**

Friday Street, Weston Subedge, Chipping Campden, Gloucestershire, GL55 6QH 01386 840192

www.seagravearms.com

f The Seagrave Arms
🐦 @theseagravearms
📷 @seagravearms

9
KOJ CHELTENHAM

This casual Japanese joint started out as a pop-up before a successful Kickstarter campaign funded a refurb and cemented its spot in central Cheltenham.

MasterChef finalist Andrew Kojima pays homage to his Japanese heritage at his first solo project, but you won't find sushi on the menu in this small, clean-lined dining space. Instead, clash sticks over grazing plates such as miso roast salmon or Koj's signature fried chicken. Upstairs, the Kampai bar offers refuge from the busy open-plan kitchen and specialises in Asian-inspired cocktails and Japanese beers.

Chef **Andrew Kojima**. 3 course lunch from **£18**. 3 course dinner from **£21**. Seats **40**

3 Regent Street, Cheltenham, Gloucestershire, GL50 1HE 01242 850455

www.kojcheltenham.co.uk

f Koj Cheltenham
🐦 @KojCheltenham
📷 @kojcheltenham

10
THE SWAN AT SOUTHROP

Set in the rather swish Thyme, this 17th century (but newly revamped) award winning pub is popular with Southrop's village community and visitors alike.

'Homegrown, homemade and produce-driven' is the motto here: each morning fresh veggies, herbs and eggs are harvested from the farm's gardens to create simple and outstandingly delicious food.

The service is charming too, and dining at The Swan provides a sense of enjoying the very best of English country living – especially when you eat outdoors in the courtyard garden.

Chef **Matthew Wardman**. 3 course lunch from **£28**. 3 course dinner from **£28**. Seats **85** inside, **45** outside

Southrop, Gloucestershire, GL7 3NX 01367 850205

www.theswanatsouthrop.co.uk

f The Swan at Southrop
🐦 @SwanSouthrop
📷 @thyme.england

Wiltshire

No 16
THE BELL

Wiltshire

Restaurants listed in the guide correspond to the numbers plotted on the map.

■ Higher member | ■ Member

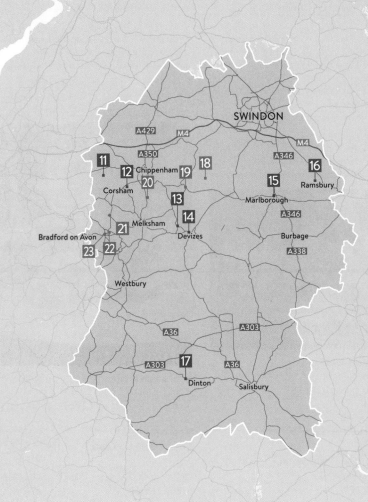

SWINDON

A429

M4

A350

11

12 Chippenham

Corsham

20

18

19

A346

M4

16

15

Ramsbury

Marlborough

13

A346

14

21 Melksham

Devizes

Burbage

Bradford on Avon

A338

23 22

Westbury

A36

A303

17

A303

A36

Dinton Salisbury

Locations are approximate.

11 Ⓐ Ⓢ

RESTAURANT HYWEL JONES BY LUCKNAM PARK

Lap of luxury near Bath

Hats off to Hywel Jones, the chef who has held a Michelin star here since 2006.

Savour his fabulous cooking in the regal restaurant (go all out with the superb seven course tasting menu) or relax in the informal brasserie. Whichever you choose, as you arrive via the mile-long tree-lined avenue, you'll get the sense that Lucknam is about more than just good food.

Inside, the Palladian mansion is adorned with exquisite furnishings and antiques. Outside lies 500 acres of parkland, best explored on horseback from the equestrian centre. Oh, and there's a sleek spa and cookery school, too.

Chef **Hywel Jones**
3 course Sunday lunch from **£45**
3 course dinner from **£87**
Seats **64**
Bedrooms **42**
Room rate from **£275**

Colerne, near Chippenham,
Wiltshire, SN14 8AZ
01225 742777

www.lucknampark.co.uk

f Lucknam Park Hotel & Spa
🐦 @lucknampark
📷 @lucknam_park

12 Ⓢ

THE METHUEN ARMS

Nose–to–tail dining

With gorgeous dining pub food available from breakfast to dinner, and menus combining classic appeal with smart creativity, it's no surprise that The Methuen Arms is well established on the foodie radar.

Chef Leigh Evans has a passion for dishes which draw on and represent the surrounding landscape. He's also a keen proponent of nose-to-tail-cooking, so nothing good is wasted.

Explore Leigh's menus in the beautifully restored Georgian inn, which sits alongside the stately home and parkland of Corsham Court.

Chef **Leigh Evans**
3 course lunch from **£29.50**
3 course dinner from **£29.50**
Seats **125**
Bedrooms **19**
Room rate from **£140**

2 High Street, Corsham, Wiltshire, SN13 0HB
01249 717060

www.themethuenarms.com

f The Methuen Arms
🐦 @MethuenArms
📷 @themethuenarms

13 ⓢ

THE GEORGE & DRAGON
Country character

Cosy up by an inglenook fireplace and dine on sumptuous seafood at this 16th century coaching inn. It's the house speciality, delivered daily after being landed at St Mawes in Cornwall.

However, it's not only seafood that Wiltshire gourmets return for: local meats and game dishes have also earned the inn two AA rosettes.

A new garden terrace adds an alfresco option for warmer days, while bespoke bedrooms promise sweet slumber after a good dinner.

Events such as quiz nights and barbecues also feature regularly.

Chef **Tom Bryant & Christopher Day**
2 course lunch/dinner from **£17.50**
3 course lunch/dinner from **£22.50**
Seats **40**
Bedrooms **3**
Room rate from **£75**

High Street, Rowde, Wiltshire, SN10 2PN
01380 723053

www.thegeorgeanddragonrowde.co.uk

f The George & Dragon
🐦 @_thegandd
📷 @thegandd_

No 20
SIGN OF
THE ANGEL

14 ⑤

THE PEPPERMILL
Devizes foodie hub

With an award winning restaurant, expertly stocked wine bar and bijou collection of five-star rated bedrooms, The Peppermill ticks all the boxes for a greedy weekend in Wiltshire.

Occupying a roomy building in the centre of the charming market town, this casual dining spot is popular with locals for smart lunches and indulgent dinners. It's also famed for its extensive cocktail list and collection of 100 wines by the bottle (yes, you read that correctly).

The restaurant offers a contemporary British line-up of dishes crafted from Wiltshire produce – think celeriac and mushroom croquettes, pork tenderloin stuffed with figs, prunes and apricots, followed by chocolate brownie with cherry compote.

3 course lunch from **£20**
3 course dinner from **£26**
Seats **60**
Bedrooms **7**
Room rate from **£115**

40 St John's Street, Devizes,
Wiltshire, SN10 1BL
01380 710407

www.peppermilldevizes.co.uk

f The Peppermill
🐦 @peppermilldev
📷 @peppermilldevizes

15

RICK STEIN, MARLBOROUGH
Iconic dishes in a Grade II-listed house

It isn't just the classic Stein's dishes that wow guests at this delightful seafood brasserie; diners at the Marlborough branch can also savour its location at the stunning Lloran House. It's a gem of beautiful bow windows and tasteful brasserie decor.

The food is just as charming, with iconic seafood dishes such as dover sole à la meunière and turbot hollandaise served alongside sumptuous plates of baked guinea fowl with garlic beans and smoked sausage.

Don't miss the weekday set menus, traditional Sunday roast and decent vegetarian options.

Chef **Kevin Chandler**
3 course lunch from **£24.95**
3 course dinner from **£30**
Seats **80**

Lloran House, 42a High Street,
Marlborough, Wiltshire, SN8 1HQ
01672 233333

www.rickstein.com

f Rick Stein, Marlborough
🐦 @steinmarlb
📷 @ricksteinrestaurants

16 Ⓢ Ⓐ
THE BELL
Hyper–local village dining

A 300-year-old coaching inn, The Bell is a handsome building standing proudly on The Square in the village of Ramsbury.

It's part of the Ramsbury Estate which guarantees a steady supply of produce for the chef – not just from the kitchen garden but also from the distillery, brewery and smokehouse.

Menus are an artfully constructed mix of modern European cuisine and pub classics. Indulge in steak and kidney pie, homemade burgers or a fisherman's sharing board – complete with Ramsbury Vodka-cured trout – before retiring to one of nine luxurious rooms.

3 course lunch from **£24**
3 course dinner from **£24**
Seats **42**
Bedrooms **9**
Room rate from **£110**

The Square, Ramsbury, Marlborough, Wiltshire, SN8 2PE
01672 520230

www.ramsbury.com

f The Bell at Ramsbury
🐦 @thebellramsbury
📷 @bell_ramsbury

17 Ⓢ
HOWARD'S HOUSE HOTEL
Kitchen garden gourmet

In the pretty village of Teffont Evias lies a small, independent hotel that has won countless accolades for its outstanding food, service and romantic ambience.

You'll find nine comfortable refurbished bedrooms, a smart Coach House for parties and meetings, and a busy calendar of edible events – from gourmet getaways to foraging experiences with new head chef Andy Britton.

Andy trained under Albert Roux and Michael Caines and produces superb English cooking in tune with the seasons; local ingredients include eggs and veg from the kitchen garden.

Chef **Andy Britton**
Lunch plates from **£7.95**
3 course dinner from **£33.50**
Seats **22**
Bedrooms **9**
Room rate from **£95**

Teffont Evias, Salisbury, Wiltshire, SP3 5RJ
01722 716392

www.howardshousehotel.co.uk

f Howard's House Hotel
🐦 @howards_house
📷 @howardshouse_hotel

Unique eats

9 Koj Cheltenham

Don't visit Cheltenham's fast-casual Asian spot in search of the usual sushi or chicken katsu. Instead, delight in fine grazing-style Japanese dishes such as miso roast cod and beef tataki from *MasterChef* finalist Andrew Kojima.

25 Box-E

This shipping container-turned-hip dining joint on Bristol's Wapping Wharf must be one of Britain's smallest restaurants. Book a stool at the 'kitchen table' and watch Elliott Lidstone in action in the open-plan kitchen.

36 Menu Gordon Jones

Expect the unexpected at this cathedral to culinary curiosities: cepe mousse, peach melba bao buns and Weetabix ice cream have all featured on chef patron Gordon Jones' secret tasting menus.

122 Appleton's Bar & Restaurant

Classic Italian dishes meet contemporary Cornish cuisine at Andy Appleton's first solo venture. Plankton-infused tortellini and prosecco-battered polenta are served with wine from the vineyard.

85 Glazebrook House Hotel

Lose yourself in a wonderland of theatrical decor and fine food and wine at this fabulously idiosyncratic country house hotel.

18 [S]
THE WHITE HORSE INN

A warm welcome, inviting dishes and an ever-evolving line-up of locally brewed ales come as standard at The White Horse in the heart of rural Wiltshire.

At this Michelin-mentioned pub, chef Roger Hawkshaw's gourmet offering ranges from pub classics (try the stonking seasonal burger) to chef's specials. Sourcing only the freshest of ingredients – often from Compton Bassett's abundance of smallholdings – each dish guarantees a seasonal taste of the terroir.

Chef **Roger Hawkshaw**. 3 course lunch from **£15**. 3 course dinner from **£35**. Seats **42**. Bedrooms **8**. Room rate from **£85**

Compton Bassett, Calne, Wiltshire, SN11 8RG
01249 813118
www.whitehorse-comptonbassett.co.uk

f The White Horse Inn, Compton Bassett
🐦 @WhiteHorseCB

19 [S]
LANSDOWNE STRAND

Local family brewery Arkell's, which this year celebrates 175 years in business, has owned this historic coaching inn for the past decade. The elegantly refurbished ground floor features graceful period features, open fireplaces, a charming panelled snug and private dining rooms. Book a table in the popular two AA rosette restaurant which serves seasonal, locally sourced modern British dishes with considerable flair. Or head to the comfy lounge for quality brasserie-style food including home-smoked salmon and pickled cucumber sandwiches, and Malthouse Craft Lager-battered fish and chips.

Chef **Joel Lear**. 3 course lunch from **£19.95**. 3 course dinner from **£26.50**. Seats **45**. Bedrooms **25**. Room rate from **£80**

The Strand, Calne, Wiltshire, SN11 0EH
01249 812488
www.lansdownestrand.co.uk

f Lansdowne Strand
🐦 @LansdowneStrand
📷 @lansdowne_strand

20 [S]
SIGN OF THE ANGEL

It's worth making a trip to this ancient coaching inn in the National Trust village of Lacock just to revel in the 600 years of history worn into its oak-panelled walls, low-slung beams and sloping ceilings. The fact that Sign of the Angel is also a hub for fabulous food and drink is an added bonus.

Rustic dishes crafted from locally sourced, seasonal ingredients feel right in the wood-heavy dining rooms. Grab a spot by the fire and settle in with three courses of greedy gratification and a glass of something good. The full 15th century experience can be enjoyed by booking a night in a charming bedroom.

Chef **Jonathan Furby**. 3 course lunch from **£22**. 3 course dinner from **£32**. Seats **50**. Bedrooms **5**. Room rate from **£110**

Church Street, Lacock, Wiltshire, SN15 2LB
01249 730230
www.signoftheangel.co.uk

f Sign of the Angel
🐦 @SignoftheAngel
📷 @signoftheangel

21 [A]
THE LONGS ARMS

Opposite a medieval church in the sleepy village of South Wraxall sits this charming bay-windowed pub. Visit for cask ales, exposed beams, wonky eaves and friendly, relaxed dining – indoors or alfresco. Landlord and talented head chef Robert Allcock produces accomplished British dishes packed with flavour. Bread, chocolates, smoked meats and fish: it's all proudly made in house using carefully sourced local and seasonal ingredients. Nods from the national press and a proudly unpretentious reputation has earned The Longs Arms a firm fanbase of locals and visitors alike.

Chef **Rob Allcock**. 3 course lunch from **£28**. 3 course dinner from **£28**. Seats **35**

South Wraxall, Bradford on Avon, Wiltshire, BA15 2SB
01225 864450
www.thelongsarms.com

f The Longs Arms
🐦 @thelongsarms
📷 @the_longs_arms

22 [S]
THE GEORGE AT WOOLLEY

There are three unique dining spaces to choose from at this Wiltshire inn, so whether you want to cosy up by the inglenook fire, watch the team of chefs in the theatre kitchen or catch up with friends in the Pantry dining room, there's a spot for every occasion.

Supper is best started with a G&T – the bar boasts a healthy collection – before browsing the à la carte menu of European dishes. Experienced chef Alex Venables oversees the classically trained team: expect favourites such as beef wellington executed with skill and presented in style.

Chef **Alexander Venables**. 3 course lunch from **£19.95**. 3 course dinner from **£17.95**. Seats **90**. Bedrooms **2**. Room rate from **£120**

67 Woolley Street, Bradford on Avon, Wiltshire, BA15 1AQ
01225 865650
www.thegeorgebradfordonavon.co.uk

f The George
🐦 @thegeorgeatboa

23
THE BUNCH OF GRAPES

With steaming bowls of moules marinière, steak frites and carafes crowding the tables, you could easily be in the backstreets of southwestern France at this bistro in Bradford on Avon.

Classic Gallic dishes are fashioned over flames by head chef Steve Carss via Bertha, the wood-burning oven. Weekly changing market and classic menus offer seasonal small plates, gastropub-style dishes or refined three course options, while the impeccable wine list showcases bottles imported directly from the vineyards. Stop by mid-morning at the weekend for brunch.

Chef **Steve Carss**. 3 course lunch from **£26**. 3 course dinner from **£32**. Seats **80**

14 Silver Street, Bradford on Avon, Wiltshire, BA15 1JY
01225 938088
www.thebunchofgrapes.com

f The Bunch Of Grapes
🐦 @thegrapesboa
📷 @thegrapesboa

Bristol & Bath

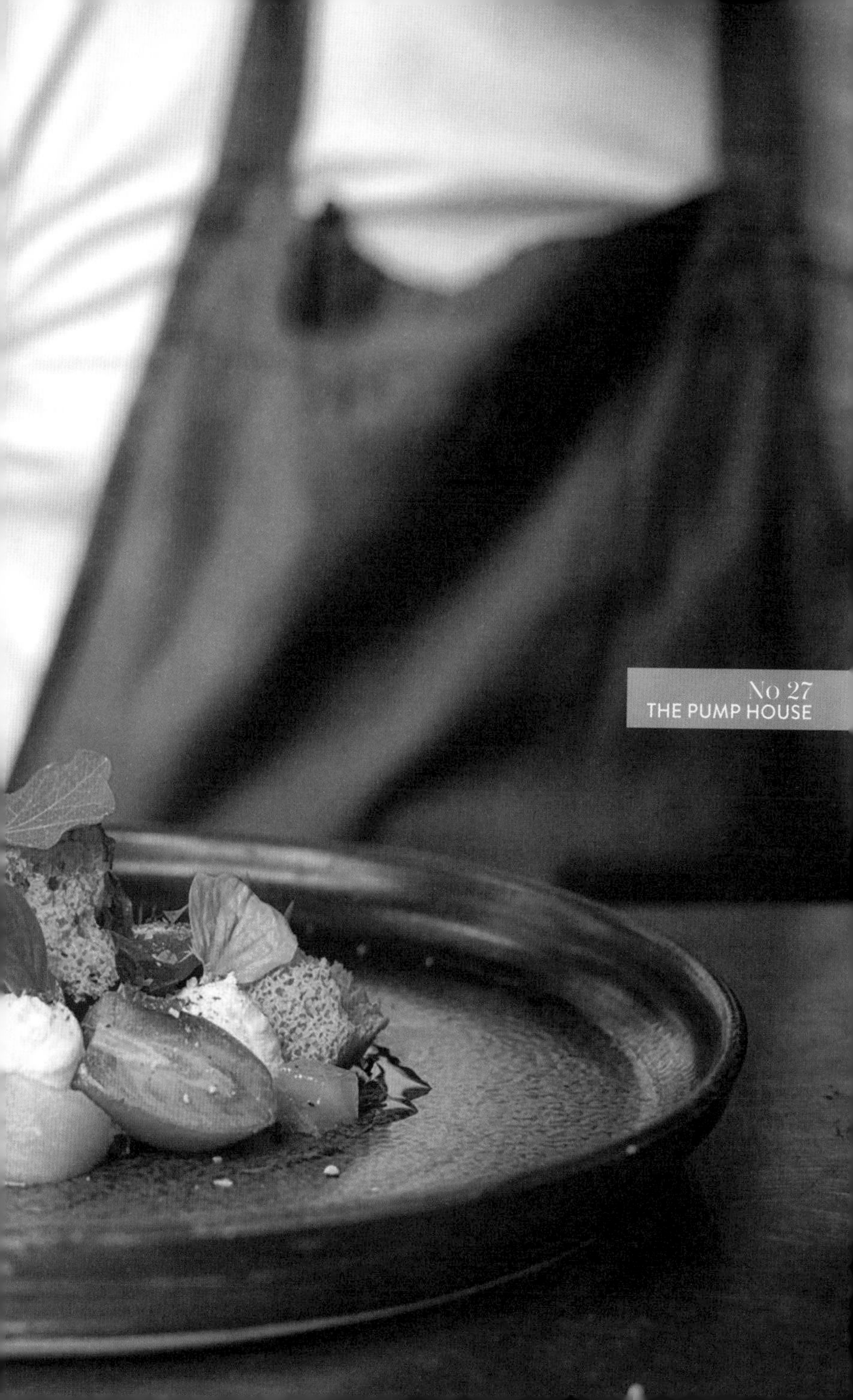

No 27
THE PUMP HOUSE

Bristol & Bath

Restaurants listed in the guide correspond to the numbers plotted on the map.

■ Higher member | ■ Member

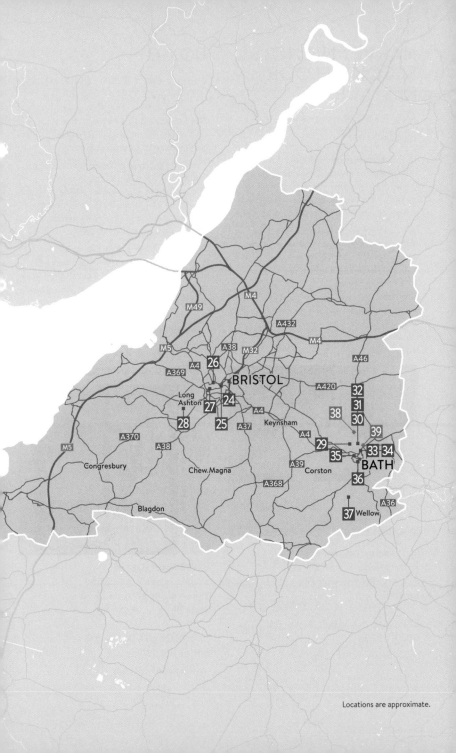

BRISTOL

Long
Ashton

Keynsham

Corston

BATH

Congresbury

Chew Magna

Blagdon

Wellow

M49

M4

M5

A4

A369

A38

M32

A432

M4

A46

A420

A4

A37

A4

A4

A370

A38

A39

A368

M5

A36

26

24

27

25

28

32

31

30

38

39

29

35

33

34

36

37

HARVEY NICHOLS SECOND FLOOR RESTAURANT

Decadent glamour in the city

This sophisticated spot will delight any foodie with a taste for luxury. Dripping in gold – from the leather banquettes to the ceilings to the curtains – the two AA rosette restaurant exudes decadence and gorgeous indulgence.

Leith-trained, award winning chef Louise McCrimmon's dishes are as alluring as the decor. Her deft touch combines well-loved seasonal flavours to produce British dishes with a nod to French cooking. Breakfast and afternoon tea are also available to inspire all-day extravagance. Meals are complemented with sippables from an extensive wine list, and be sure to arrive early for an aperitif at the lavish cocktail bar.

Chef **Louise McCrimmon**
3 course lunch from **£22**
3 course dinner from **£22**
Seats **65**

27 Philadelphia Street, Bristol, BS1 3BZ
01179 168898
www.harveynichols.com

f Harvey Nichols
🐦 @harveynichols
📷 @harveynichols

BOX-E

Contemporary container cooking

This minuscule, 14-cover joint is housed in two converted shipping containers within Bristol's hip Wapping Wharf development.

There's no shortage of takers for its seasonal British cooking, so book ahead to get in. Recommended in *The Michelin Guide 2018*, the focus here is on super-fresh local produce, simply prepared and served in relaxed surroundings with friendly service.

The 'kitchen table' (comprised of four stools) is just centimetres away from all the cheffy action and it's here that you get to chow down on an unwritten tasting menu served by head chef Elliott. Check out the interesting wine list too, which features biodynamic, organic and sustainable wines.

Photo: André Pattenden

Chef **Elliott Lidstone**
3 course lunch from **£27.50**
3 course dinner from **£27.50**
Seats **18**

Unit 10, Cargo 1, Wapping Wharf, Bristol, BS1 6WP
www.boxebristol.com

🐦 @boxebristol
📷 @boxebristol

MINT ROOM – BRISTOL

Re-imagining the traditional

Executive chef Saravan Nambirajan uses his Michelin-starred restaurant experience to craft original and creative dishes which are rooted in the traditions of Indian cuisine.

The Mint Room (which has a sister restaurant in Bath) is recognised by many as the finest upmarket modern Indian restaurant in Bristol.

Inside, the decor mixes past and present: ornate mirrors, large lanterns and richly painted walls rub shoulders with modern wooden furniture, exposed brick walls and an ultra modern bar. Start the evening with a cocktail and enjoy perusing a menu rich with high quality local ingredients. The choices are plentiful and include an impressive menu for vegans, as well as a tasting menu with wine flight.

Chef **Saravan Nambirajan**
3 course lunch from **£45**
3 course dinner from **£50**
Seats **68**

12-16 Clifton Road, Clifton, Bristol, BS8 1AF
01173 291300

www.mintroom.co.uk

f The Mint Room
🐦 @themintroom
📷 @themintroom

CHEF'S TIP

Dan Moon, head chef at The Gainsborough Bath Spa (No 34)

'I'm looking forward to visiting The Salutation Inn (No 74) later this year – it's right on the doorstep of where I grew up.

'I went to college with head chef Tom and I can't wait to sample some of his spectacular food.'

WINNER
2018
TRENCHERMAN'S
AWARDS
AWARD FOR
BEST BAR LIST

27
THE PUMP HOUSE
Foodie drinking den

Locals flock to this waterside city spot to explore the gargantuan gin menu, feast with friends on the excellent food at the fine dining restaurant upstairs, or grab a bite on the terrace.

On days when Bristol isn't blessed with good weather, gourmets in the know still seek shelter at the canalside Victorian pump house. With a roomy restaurant, mezzanine dining space and one of the best-stocked bars in the country, there are few better places to hunker down.

Modern British menus are guided by the seasons, with plenty of foraged and unusual ingredients packed into dishes that change daily. Treat yourself to delights such as English carrot with kombucha alongside revamped classics such as pork belly with puy lentils and smoked garlic mash.

Chef **Nick Fenlon**
3 course lunch from **£22**
3 course dinner from **£30**
Seats **80**

Merchants Road, Hotwells,
Bristol, BS8 4PZ
01179 272229
www.the-pumphouse.com

f The Pump House, Bristol
🐦 @pumphsebristol
📷 @pumphousebristol

28

THE BIRD IN HAND

Foraged feasting

Bristol's culinary credentials bubble over into the suburbs at this popular pub in Long Ashton.

Simple ingredients and foraged finds take centre stage on chef patron Toby Gritten's seasonally shifting menus. Rustic dining is infused with Bristol boho in dishes such as fried semolina with gnocchi, garnished with squash, alliums and strained kefir.

The bustling bar is a busy hub on weekend evenings so you'll need to arrive early – or be prepared to wrestle a local – to secure a spot. There are lots of options though, such as the fireside snug which is a cosy place to perch if you're sampling the 40-strong gin collection. The spacious dining room provides a more formal setting for dinner.

Chefs **Felix Rayment & Toby Gritten**
3 course lunch from **£25**
3 course dinner from **£30**
Seats **26**

17 Weston Road, Long Ashton,
Somerset, BS41 9LA
01275 395222

www.bird-in-hand.co.uk

f Bird In Hand
🐦 @birdinhand2011
📷 @birdinhandlongashton

29 Ⓐ Ⓢ

THE BATH PRIORY

Elegant city retreat

It's no surprise that one of the country's most elegant cities is home to this splendidly refined hotel, restaurant and spa.

The Bath Priory may be just a short walk from the busy city centre, but it's a peaceful haven due to the four acres of walled gardens surrounding the honey-coloured manor house. The dining experience makes full use of the garden through homegrown produce on the menus and views from the light-filled restaurant.

Dishes are immaculate, extolling the beauty of subtly balanced flavours and drawing on the global culinary experiences of executive chef Michael Nizzero.

Pleasingly, à la carte and tasting menus include decent vegetarian and vegan options, too.

Chef **Michael Nizzero**
3 course lunch from **£30**
3 course dinner from **£85**
Seats **72**
Bedrooms **33**
Room rate from **£215**

Weston Road, Bath, BA1 2XT
01225 331922

www.thebathpriory.co.uk

f The Bath Priory
🐦 @thebathpriory
📷 @brownswordhotels

Nose— to—tail eating

12 The Methuen Arms

Whether you're visiting for a trad pub lunch or classic à la carte dinner, head chef Leigh Evans crafts seasonal dishes such as corned beef on sourdough toast, seared calf's liver and whole roasted plaice.

83 The Millbrook Inn

French chef JP Bidart ensures every last morsel of the locally sourced meat delivered to his south Devon kitchen is put to good use in dishes such as pig trotter and foie gras patty.

40 The Redan Inn

Often-overlooked ingredients (onglet steak, partridge and rabbit) make regular appearances at this rural dining pub and share the limelight with foraged finds on a hyper seasonal line-up.

31 Star & Garter

All of the Cornish-reared meat arriving in the kitchen of this Falmouth dining pub is butchered, cured and even smoked by head chef Andrew Richardson and team. Expect homemade salami, smoked brisket and slow-cooked lamb shoulder among the meaty marvels.

123 Jamie Oliver's Fifteen Cornwall

Root-to-shoot eating and nose-to-tail philosophies buddy up on Adam Banks' Italian-inspired menus. Fermentation and pickling are also used to preserve the Cornish crop.

THE MARLBOROUGH TAVERN

British classics in the heart of Bath

A stone's throw from the sweeping grandeur of Bath's Royal Crescent is a local that's loved by residents and visitors alike.

The Marlborough Tavern's cosy log fire, walled garden and 18th century interior are a magnet for weary sightseers seeking refreshment.

Dan Edwards crafts modern British feasts such as cured salmon with wasabi mayo, followed by a trio of beef and rounded off with blood orange crème brûlée. The inn stays true to its pub roots too: those hankering after a steak or burger will find plenty of hearty classics on the two AA rosette menu.

Chef **Dan Edwards**
3 course lunch from **£26.50**
3 course dinner from **£26.50**
Seats **76**

35 Marlborough Buildings, Bath, BA1 2LY
01225 423731

www.marlborough-tavern.com

f The Marlborough Tavern, Bath
🐦 @marlboroughtav
📷 @marlboroughtavern

THE CHEQUERS

Gastro–Georgian

Serving the city's culture-seeking tourists and local gourmets since 1776, The Chequers is just around the corner from Bath hot-spots the Circus and Royal Crescent.

Chef Alex Betts creates award winning, inventive British dishes, displayed in modern pub classics like salt and pepper squid as well as fine dining dishes such as monkfish, serrano ham and king oyster mushrooms.

Relaxed dining is echoed in the elegant pubby decor where parquet floor and mirrored panels are complemented by cushioned pews and (upstairs) an open view of the culinary brigade at work. The fine wine list and draft beer collection should be sampled, too.

Chef **Alex Betts**
3 course lunch from **£23.50**
3 course dinner from **£25.50**
Seats **76**

50 Rivers Street, Bath, BA1 2QA
01225 360017

www.thechequersbath.com

f Chequers Bath
🐦 @chequersbath
📷 @chequersbath

32 Ⓐ Ⓢ

THE OLIVE TREE RESTAURANT
Picture–worthy plating

You'll find The Olive Tree Restaurant in the belly of the fabulously quirky Queensberry Hotel. The relaxed glamour and refreshing informality that courses through the Bath townhouse is beautifully balanced by head chef Chris Cleghorn's incredible attention to detail and panache for impeccable plating.

Start your experience in style with a glass of fizz in the courtyard or a cocktail in the newly refurbished Old Q Bar, before heading to the basement to thoroughly spoil yourself with the seasonal tasting menu. Restaurant manager Roman Vidal's wine selection includes intriguing finds, and be sure to book one of the bespoke bedrooms.

Chef **Chris Cleghorn**
3 course lunch from **£30**
3 course dinner from **£50**
Seats **55**
Bedrooms **29**
Room rate from **£125**

The Queensberry Hotel, 4-7 Russel Street, Bath, BA1 2QF
01225 447928

www.olivetreebath.co.uk

f Olive Tree, Bath
🐦 @olivetreebath
📷 @olivetreebath

33

ACORN
Creative vegetarianism

The popularity of plant-based cooking may have exploded in the past year, but Richard Buckley has been serving exclusively vegetarian dishes at his Bath bistro since 2013.

Reinventing vegetarianism's reputation, owner Richard and head chef Jamie Taylor blend traditional and contemporary techniques to craft beautiful courses worthy of a place on anyone's Insta feed. Classic combinations such as leek and potato are given the fine dining treatment – charred leeks with melusine cheese dauphinoise and smoked potato brik pastry in this particular pairing.

Acorn's simple dining space has an intriguing past: formerly the house of philanthropist Ralph Allen, the historic building was the birthplace of the modern postal service.

Chefs **Richard Buckley & Jamie Taylor**
3 course lunch from **£22.95**
3 course dinner from **£36.95**
Seats **32**

2 North Parade Passage, Bath, BA1 1NX
01225 446059

www.acornrestaurant.co.uk

f Acorn Restaurant Bath
🐦 @acornvegetarian
📷 @acornrestaurant

THE GAINSBOROUGH BATH SPA

Five star dine and spa

With its vibrant and modern interpretation of classic hotel design, beautiful Georgian architecture and exquisite dining, it's not hard to understand why The Gainsborough was awarded AA Hotel of the Year.

Admire the impressive wine wall before enjoying three AA rosette cuisine from Dan Moon at The Gainsborough Restaurant. Dishes include the likes of roasted loin of Mendip venison with goat's curd and salt baked celeriac.

The hotel taps in to Bath's natural thermal springs, so plump for a spa day to take the waters in luxury, enjoy a choice of spa treatments and indulge in a delicious two course spa lunch or elegant afternoon tea.

Chef **Dan Moon**
3 course lunch from **£18**
3 course dinner from **£46**
Seats **68**
Bedrooms **99**
Room rate from **£290**

Beau Street, Bath, BA1 1QY
01225 358888

www.thegainsboroughbathspa.co.uk

f The Gainsborough Bath Spa
🐦 @gainsbathspa
📷 @thegainsboroughbathspa

MINT ROOM – BATH

Pan–Indian cuisine with modern flair

Combining the vibrancy and flavour of Indian cuisine with a blast of contemporary flair, the Mint Room provides an appealing and unusual dining experience.

Inside, it's chic and spacious with subdued lighting which makes dinner delightfully intimate. Dishes coming out of the kitchen are works of art, with high quality meat, seafood, vegetables and pulses fashioned into picture-worthy plates.

Alongside traditional curries are new classics to intrigue the palate such as oven-roasted marinated venison with marrow cardamom gravy. There's also a new rooftop bar where you can enjoy a glass of champagne and small plates from the bar food menu in a cosy outdoor setting.

Chef **Soyful Alom**
3 course lunch from **£40**
3 course dinner from **£40**
Seats **80**

Longmead Gospel Hall, Lower Bristol Road, Bath, BA2 3EB
01225 446656

www.mintroom.co.uk

f The Mint Room
🐦 @themintroom
📷 @themintroom

36

MENU GORDON JONES

Extraordinary feasting

Reindeer moss, snail caviar and puffball mushrooms may not be standard dining fare, but revelling in the extraordinary is all part of the experience at this eccentric eatery.

Michelin-trained chef patron Gordon Jones has a legion of local suppliers guiding his daring – and occasionally outlandish – daily tasting menus. Abandon any assumptions and let the team reveal the magic in five course lunch and six course supper experiences. Pair the incredible edibles with a glass or two from Gordon's impressive list of biodynamic and organic wines.

Chef **Gordon Jones**
3 course lunch from **£50**
3 course dinner from **£55**
Seats **24**

2 Wellsway, Bath, BA2 3AQ
01225 480871

www.menugordonjones.co.uk

f Menu Gordon Jones
🐦 @menugordonjones
📷 @menugordonjones

37 Ⓢ

THE WHEATSHEAF COMBE HAY

Quirky countryside haven

You'll receive a tail-wagging welcome from resident spaniels Margaux, Gloria and Brie when you pay a visit to The Wheatsheaf Combe Hay.

A haven for both dog lovers and pooch-less patrons, the peaceful rural setting is an ideal launch pad for all sorts of outdoorsy adventures – or just a stroll around the huge garden.

After your explorations, settle down in the highly regarded restaurant. Chef Eddy Rains and his crew craft modern British dishes using the freshest local produce – including pickings from The Wheatsheaf's own kitchen garden – to complement ingredients such as South West scallops and Cornish hake.

Chef **Eddy Rains**
3 course lunch from **£24**
3 course dinner from **£24**
Seats **55**
Bedrooms **4**
Room rate from **£120**

Combe Hay, Bath, BA2 7EG
01225 833504

www.wheatsheafcombehay.co.uk

f The Wheatsheaf, Combe Hay
🐦 @wheatsheaf_bath
📷 @wheatsheafbath

More Bristol & Bath

38
THE HARE AND HOUNDS

Stroll up the lavender-lined path and you'll be stopped in your tracks by the panoramic views across the countryside from this Lansdown Road pub. Then take a seat on the sunny terrace with a tipple from the extensive wine and beer list and gaze across Solsbury Hill while you pique your appetite.

Inside, dark wood interiors, a long ornate bar and cosy fireside armchairs provide the setting for chef Pravin Nayar's modern British fare, where pub classics share a menu with the likes of venison croquettes, and hake and palourde clams.

Chef **Pravin Nayar**. 3 course lunch from **£23.50**. 3 course dinner from **£23.50**. Seats **108**

Lansdown Road, Bath, BA1 5TJ
01225 482682
www.hareandhoundsbath.com

f   The Hare and Hounds
🐦 @harehoundsbath
📷 @harehoundsbath

39
KING WILLIAM

This independently owned pub is a local favourite for its modern Bath feel: elegant Georgian simplicity with a big dose of comfort and hospitality.

You'll find simple furniture with crisp white linen and candlesticks reflected in gilt mirrors, and a bar stocking an impressive selection of fine wines, real ales and craft beers.

Chef James Harris (who trained with Chris Staines at Allium) creates menus which mix comfort with a frisson of flair. Be inspired by dishes such as braised rabbit leg terrine, pickled salsify, rhubarb and endive – and we dare you to resist the cornflake tart dessert.

Chef **James Harris**. 3 course lunch from **£19.95**. 3 course dinner from **£24.95**. Seats **50**

36 Thomas Street, Bath, BA1 5NN
01225 428096
www.kingwilliampub.com

🐦 @kingwilliampub

Somerset

Restaurants listed in the guide correspond to the numbers plotted on the map.

 Higher member | Member

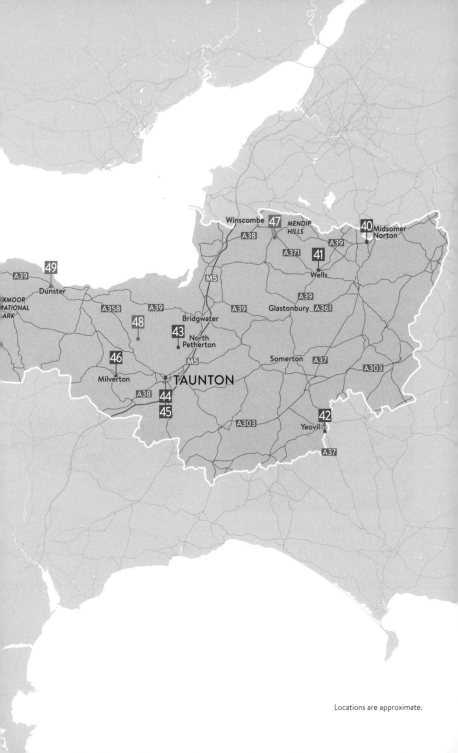

Winscombe

47 *MENDIP HILLS*

A38

40 Midsomer Norton

A371

A39

41

Wells

49

A39

Dunster

XMOOR ATIONAL ARK

A358

A39

M5

Bridgwater

48

43 North Petherton

A39

Glastonbury

A361

A39

46

Milverton

M5

Somerton

A37

A303

TAUNTON

A38

44

45

A303

42 Yeovil

A37

Locations are approximate.

THE REDAN INN

Greedy country getaway

It's fortunate there are seven boutique bedrooms above this Somerset inn, as the choice of over 100 gins behind the bar can easily lead to fraught designated driver discussions.

And with oak-beamed ceilings, charming original features and a couple of free-standing bathtubs in the bedrooms, there are plenty of additional reasons to book a greedy getaway at the dining pub.

Weekend revellers are rewarded with a short and sweet seasonal menu, which chef patron Toby Gritten executes according to a nose-to-tail philosophy. If you're celebrating, push the boat out with the five course field-to-fork tasting menu and accompanying gin flight.

Chef **Toby Gritten**
3 course lunch from **£21**
3 course dinner from **£25**
Seats **45**
Bedrooms **7**
Room rate from **£95**

Fry's Well, Chilcompton, Radstock, BA3 4HA
01761 258560
www.theredaninn.co.uk

f The Redan Inn
🐦 @theredaninn2015
📷 @theredaninn

GOODFELLOWS

Modern Mediterranean in historic Wells

Just off the marketplace in the centre of the historic city of Wells, Goodfellows offers diners a twist on modern Mediterranean cuisine, inspired by chef patron Adam Fellows' training in some of the best restaurants in Europe.

Using the finest West Country produce, including daily deliveries of fish fresh from Brixham, Adam creates inspiring and seasonally changing dishes. Fish is the house speciality, but his creative approach is equally evident in meat and vegetarian options. An open-plan kitchen adds to the theatre and creates an intimate atmosphere which celebrates exquisite flavours, fine wines and good company.

Chef **Adam Fellows**
3 course lunch from **£27**
3 course dinner from **£35**
Seats **50**

5 Sadler Street, Wells, Somerset, BA5 2RR
01749 673866
www.goodfellowswells.co.uk

f Goodfellows Restaurant, Wells
🐦 @goodfellowseat

42 Ⓐ Ⓢ

LITTLE BARWICK HOUSE

Countryside classic

Hidden away in countryside on the edge of Yeovil, Little Barwick is an insider's find for top-notch dining.

Tim and Emma Ford's comfortable and attractive restaurant with rooms delivers a taste of the very best of British cooking.

Start with a glass of fizz and canapés by the fire in the convivial sitting room, chat to other guests, then head in for a well designed and adroitly executed dinner.

Dishes are paired with an exceptional wine list and served with deft and friendly service.

Chefs **Tim Ford & Adam Bond**
3 course lunch from **£31.95**
3 course dinner from **£54.95**
Seats **40**
Bedrooms **7**
Room rate from **£110**

Rexes Hollow Lane, Barwick, near Yeovil, Somerset, BA22 9TD
01935 423902
www.littlebarwickhouse.co.uk

f Little Barwick House
🐦 @littlebarwick

43 Ⓐ

CLAVELSHAY BARN RESTAURANT

Off-the-beaten-track farmhouse dining

A converted 18th century stone barn on a working dairy farm is the rustic setting for this most rural of restaurants. Hidden away in a wooded valley on the edge of the beautiful Quantock Hills, it's a tranquil spot for a romantic rendezvous, family celebration or get-together with friends.

Owner Sue Milverton and team pride themselves on their use of local produce which is sourced from a wealth of West Country farmers and growers. Newly appointed head chef John Godfrey fashions simple rustic food to reflect the seasons – in summer, take lunch alfresco in the beautiful garden.

Chef **John Godfrey**
Lunch from **£12**
3 course dinner from **£30**
Seats **40**

Lower Clavelshay Farm, North Petherton, Bridgwater, Somerset, TA6 6PJ
01278 662629
www.clavelshaybarn.co.uk

f Clavelshay Barn Restaurant
🐦 @clavelshaybarn
📷 @clavelshaybarn

44
AUGUSTUS
Refined but relaxed

There's a high-quality gourmet experience to be had at this friendly and informal neighbourhood bistro. But you need to be in the know about Augustus, as you'd be unlikely to stumble across its location, tucked away in a little courtyard in Taunton.

Richard Guest's à la carte menus are simple and classic, inspired by a fusion of French, British and Asian influences.

On fine days, dine – complete with a glass of expertly chosen wine – in the charming courtyard, while the intimate dining room provides a lovely setting in which to linger over dinner.

Chef **Richard Guest**
3 course lunch from **£30**
3 course dinner from **£30**
Seats **40**

St James Street, Taunton, Somerset, TA1 1JR
01823 324354

www.augustustaunton.co.uk

f Augustus Restaurant
🐦 @augustustaunton

45 Ⓐ Ⓢ
THE CASTLE AT TAUNTON
Culinary flair at The Castle

Culinary history runs deep in this historic building. It's been in the guardianship of the Chapman family for 68 years, and they've long championed epicurean excellence – a theme that continues today in the sophisticated cooking of head chef Liam Finnegan.

Standards remain as high as ever through local sourcing, use of organic fruit and veg and the talent behind the pass. Pull out all the stops and experience beguiling fine dining in the intimate Castle Bow restaurant or chill in the relaxed brasserie, Brazz.

Chef **Liam Finnegan**
3 course dinner from **£39**
Seats **32**
Bedrooms **44**
Room rate from **£125**

Castle Green, Taunton, Somerset, TA1 1NF
01823 272671

www.the-castle-hotel.com

f The Castle at Taunton
🐦 @castletaunton
📷 @castletaunton

CHEF'S TIP

Liam Finnegan, head chef at The Castle at Taunton
(No 45)

'Eating Richard Guest's food at Augustus (No 44) in Taunton is always an absolute pleasure.

'He's an incredibly talented chef and his skills are matched by an equally impressive front of house team.'

THE GLOBE
Hearty country cooking for a crowd

There's a friendly, family vibe at this country pub in the heart of rural Somerset.

Mark and Adele Tarry have provided a home-from-home welcome and a bill of beautiful British classics at their Grade II-listed inn for over a decade – their kids even chip in and road test dad's dishes.

Familiar favourites such as smoked salmon carpaccio, lamb shoulder stuffed with apricot and thyme, and crispy slow-cooked pork belly grace the menu, while a blackboard of specials includes regional and seasonal treats such as Cornish pollock and locally shot pheasant.

Chef **Mark Tarry**
3 course lunch from **£17**
3 course dinner from **£20**
Seats **40**
Bedrooms **2**
Room rate from **£60**

Fore Street, Milverton, Somerset, TA4 1JX
01823 400534
www.theglobemilverton.co.uk

f The Globe Milverton
🐦 @infomilverton
📷 @theglobemilverton

Rural feasting

67 The Coach House by Michael Caines

For off-the-beaten-track dining with a dash of glam, this former 17th century coaching house-turned-smart dining room excels in classic cooking served in tasteful surroundings.

42 Little Barwick House

A gem for foodies looking for a rural retreat, this restaurant with rooms is one to put on your hit list for its quality cooking, illustrious wine list and first-class guest experience.

136 Victoria Inn at Perranuthnoe

It may be hidden away in the depths of the Cornish countryside, but food sourced from surrounding fields and hedgerows, along with two beautifully converted bedrooms, make the Victoria Inn worth seeking out.

16 The Bell

Produce from the Ramsbury Estate's own brewery, distillery, smokehouse and kitchen garden take The Bell's modern European cuisine and pub classics to the next level.

121 The Cornish Arms

The Stein name is synonymous with Cornish style so, as you'd expect, Jill Stein's simple and beautiful interiors create a fabulous backdrop to Rick's family-orientated feasting.

More Somerset

47 S
THE BATH ARMS HOTEL

Country pub dining gets a modern makeover at this public house in the Somerset village of Cheddar.

Within walking distance of the historic gorge and caves, The Bath Arms received extensive refurbishment when Sean and Jacqui took over in 2014.

Six smart bedrooms complement the polished pub fare from head chef Sean Lee, making this a fab overnight find. Two alfresco dining areas offer plenty of sun-drenched supping in summer and, as you'd imagine, the cheese is pretty good.

Chef **Sean Lee**. 3 course lunch from **£21.95**. 3 course dinner from **£21.95**. Seats **70**. Bedrooms **6**. Room rate from **£85**

Bath Street, Cheddar, Somerset, BS27 3AA
01934 742425
www.batharms.com

f The Bath Arms
🐦 @bath_arms
📷 @bath_arms

48 S
THE RISING SUN INN

Rustic pub classics meet contemporary culinary combinations at this thatched inn in the Quantock Hills.

Head chef Mike Griffiths serves up crowd pleasers such as confit duck with exotic elements – star anise, chilli and ginger in this case – and sources ingredients from a network of Somerset suppliers. The Exmoor steaks, served on volcanic stones with a selection of flavoured salts to season, are a favourite with visitors and West Bagborough locals alike. Two bedrooms offer respite for weary walkers and greedy weekenders setting out for the hills.

Chef **Mike Griffiths**. 3 course lunch from **£18**. 3 course dinner from **£22**. Seats **74**. Bedrooms **2**. Room rate from **£95**

West Bagborough, Taunton, Somerset, TA4 3EF
01823 432575
www.therisingsunbagborough.co.uk

f The Rising Sun
🐦 @risingsun_pub

49 A S
THE LUTTRELL ARMS HOTEL

In the heart of the medieval village of Dunster, this boutique country house hotel, with its quirky and authentic decor, captures the spirit of the surrounding Exmoor wilds.

Roaring log fires, a traditional bar, stylish restaurant and fabulous beer garden with views over Dunster Castle offer plenty of options for foodies.

With splashes of tweed and horsey wallpaper, the AA rosette Psalter's Restaurant is a fitting canvas for head chef Barrie Tucker's creative re-interpretations of fine dining classics. The bedrooms are characterful and inviting too.

Chef **Barrie Tucker**. 3 course lunch from **£20**. 3 course dinner from **£29**. Seats **45**. Bedrooms **28**. Room rate from **£120**

32-36 High Street, Dunster, Somerset, TA24 6SG
01643 821 555
www.luttrellarms.co.uk

f The Luttrell Arms Hotel
🐦 @luttrellarms
📷 @luttrellarms

Dorset & Hampshire

No 59
CHEWTON GLEN HOTEL

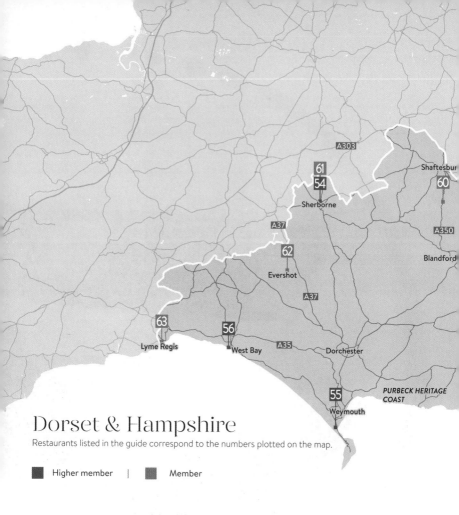

Dorset & Hampshire

Restaurants listed in the guide correspond to the numbers plotted on the map.

■ Higher member | ■ Member

Locations are approximate.

50

RICK STEIN, WINCHESTER

Smart seafood in the city

This Hampshire restaurant was Rick Stein's first venture outside Cornwall. However, it still celebrates the brand's coastal roots, sourcing the freshest fish and serving it as stylish, classic Stein dishes.

The menu displays a veritable feast of seafood specials, often with an international spin on an old fave. Try pan fried john dory fillets with a tomato and caper sauce for a Venetian twist, or the Singapore chilli crab for oriental eats.

Those who aren't angling for seafood will find an array of meat-based dishes and a generous vegetarian menu.

Chef **Chris Baker**
3 course lunch from **£24.95**
3 course dinner from **£29**
Seats **66**

7 High Street, Winchester,
Hampshire, SO23 9JX
01962 353535
www.rickstein.com

f Rick Stein, Winchester
🐦 @steinwinchester
📷 @ricksteinrestaurants

51

THE BLACK RAT

Winchester wow factor

This quirky, relaxed restaurant in Winchester town centre has proudly held Michelin star status for almost a decade.

John Marsden-Jones' generous, hearty dishes come packed with punchy flavours, while wild and unusual ingredients are supplied by The Black Rat's dedicated forager – and its kitchen garden stocked with herbs.

Cocoon yourself in the candlelit rustic interior with its eclectic furnishings, and enjoy the anticipation of great food and spot-on service. Start by picking from the bar list of over 100 carefully-selected wines and 30 gins from around the world. And if the weather's good, take it outside and dine in one of the heated thatched huts in the garden.

Chef **John Marsden-Jones**
3 course lunch from **£27.50**
3 course dinner from **£40**
Seats **40**

88 Chesil Street, Winchester,
Hampshire, SO23 0HX
01962 844465
www.theblackrat.co.uk

f The Black Rat Restaurant

THE THREE LIONS

Entente cordiale cuisine

This family-run New Forest restaurant has an impressive 22-year track record: its roll call of famous guests ranges from Murray Walker to Madonna and it's been named Hampshire Restaurant of the Year three times.

Long-serving chef patron Mike Womersley is a former Michelin-starred chef and the excellent menu of authentic, seasonal British-French dishes is freshly cooked by him, so bon appétit. Wines are thoughtfully selected from around the world, and eating in the rustic dining room is a refreshingly informal affair.

Book in for a night to enjoy the delights of two acres of lawns, shrubs and pasture – plus the outdoor hot tub.

No 62
ACORN INN

Chef **Mike Womersley**
3 course lunch from **£24.50**
3 course dinner from **£29.50**
Seats **60**
Bedrooms **7**
Room rate from **£125**

Stuckton, Fordingbridge, Hampshire, SP6 2HF
01425 652489

www.thethreelionsrestaurant.co.uk

53

RICK STEIN, SANDBANKS

Elegance by the harbour

Indulge in maritime moments – from light lunching to more formal dining – at the smart Sandbanks outpost of Stein's.

The downstairs bar is the cabin of choice for daytime dalliances fuelled by moules marinière or a spankingly fresh fillet of plaice. Watch the kitchen theatre go down as chefs plate up langoustines and oysters for lunchtime diners.

The upstairs restaurant offers stunning views across Poole harbour as evening guests tuck into Seafood Restaurant classics such as turbot hollandaise, fruits de mer, or delicious steaks for those eschewing piscatorial plates.

Chef **Pete Murt**
3 course lunch from **£25**
3 course dinner from **£31**
Seats **145**

10-14 Banks Road, Sandbanks, Poole, Dorset, BH13 7QB
01202 283000
www.rickstein.com

f Rick Stein, Sandbanks
🐦 @steinsandbanks
📷 @ricksteinrestaurants

54

THE GREEN

Adventurous modern dining

Chef Sasha Matkevich developed his love of cooking from his grandmother and the wealth of ingredients he encountered in his childhood at the foot of the Caucasus.

The importance of provenance has remained with Sasha throughout his career; he still gets excited to discover new foraged ingredients and loves to introduce diners to unusual flavours.

Visitors to the restaurant on Sherborne's historic Cheap Street can indulge in delights such as coal fish with purple potato and tarragon cream. Or try a dish or two from the zakuski sharing menu which includes the likes of butter bean hummus and charcuterie. Traditionalists make the trip on a Sunday for Sasha's sublime roasts.

Chef **Sasha Matkevich**
3 course lunch from **£22**
3 course dinner from **£27**
Seats **60**

3 The Green, Sherborne, Dorset, DT9 3HY
01935 813821
www.greenrestaurant.co.uk

f The Green Restaurant
🐦 @greensherborne

55

THE CRAB HOUSE CAFE

Fresh from the water

In a wooden shack with swoonsome views to Chesil Beach, super fresh seafood dishes are crafted on a menu that changes up to twice daily, depending on what's landed.

Unfussy, modern, wine-paired dining is the order of the day here. Fish and shellfish are harvested within 40 miles, with plump Portland oysters arriving in minutes from their beds next door, while salad is picked fresh from the kitchen garden. Tucking into a 'crab to crack' outdoors under blushed pink umbrellas makes a memorable meal – though you don't need special tools to tackle most of the dishes, such as sand sole poached in garlic and rosemary oil.

Chef **Will Smith**
3 course lunch from **£29**
3 course dinner from **£29**
Seats **40**

Ferryman's Way, Portland Road,
Weymouth, Dorset, DT4 9YU
01305 788867

www.crabhousecafe.co.uk

f The Crab House
@ @thecrabhousecafe

56

RIVERSIDE RESTAURANT

Destination seafood dining

There are few better ways to spend an afternoon in the South West than cracking shells, slurping oysters and sipping chilled champagne while enjoying views over the water. And for more than 50 years, Dorset day-trippers have flocked to Riverside Restaurant on the River Brit to get their fish fix.

Neil Chilcott certainly knows the Riverside's history as he's been involved with the restaurant for 40 years – and its owner for two. Neil honours the restaurant's legacy, with head chef Tony Shaw turning the fishermen's finest catch into classic dishes with a contemporary twist. Expect combinations such as roasted skate with chorizo and steamed clams.

Chef **Tony Shaw**
3 course lunch from **£29**
3 course dinner from **£45**
Seats **90**

West Bay, Bridport, Dorset, DT6 4EZ
01308 422011

www.thefishrestaurant-westbay.co.uk

f Riverside Restaurant
🐦 @riversidewb

Foodie families

64 The Dining Room at Saunton

Foodie families can tick all the boxes at this lively hotel overlooking one of Britain's best beaches. Surf, swim or soak in the dazzling new spa before gathering en famille for two AA rosette grill-style dining, where kids are welcome.

84 Soar Mill Cove Hotel

This family-friendly hotel, hidden away in wonderful wild countryside near Salcombe, will keep gourmets of all ages happy with its mix of cocktail bar, quality restaurant, pool, games and nearby cove for swimming.

127 The Rosevine

Let the kids run free at this chic seaside boutique hotel which is set up for family getaways. Kid-pleasing menus, a well-stocked games room and gardens will delight little ones while grown-ups swoon over head chef Tim Pile's fine dining dishes.

152 Rick Stein's Fish

Do fish 'n' chips in style at Falmouth's poshest chippy. Spankingly fresh fish and fries with all the classic trimmings are served in smart surroundings. Grown-ups can also pair their plate with a glass of Cornish fizz.

146 St Moritz Hotel

A Cornish seaside setting with family-friendly facilities is complemented by good quality cooking which meets the whole gang's requirements. And, if you stay, you can also switch up finer dining at Shorecrest with relaxed eats at the poolside Sea Side restaurant.

More Dorset & Hampshire

57 Ⓢ

THE ANCHOR INN AT LOWER FROYLE

If you're hankering after a charming English country pub with quirky interiors (this one has literary-themed rooms), hearty food (it's earned two AA rosettes for its modern twist on seasonal classics) and a stonking drinks list (the bar flows with rare wines, artisan spirits and an array of beers), The Anchor ticks all the boxes. From rich local game to fresh-off-the-boat fish, dinner in the cosy restaurant reflects the surrounding Hampshire countryside. In summer, grab a seat in the garden and soak up the rays with a local ale.

Chef **Josh Revis**. 3 course lunch from **£21**. 3 course dinner from **£30**. Seats **65**. Bedrooms **5**. Room rate from **£90**

Lower Froyle, Alton, Hampshire, GU34 4NA
01420 23261
www.anchorinnatlowerfroyle.co.uk

f The Anchor Inn at Lower Froyle
🐦 @anchorinnfroyle
📷 @anchor_inn_froyle

58 Ⓢ

THE RUNNING HORSE INN

Unpretentious service and menus of unfussy dishes are key attractions at this elegantly restored village inn on the outskirts of Winchester.

There's a spacious outdoor area for alfresco drinks and dining, or you can seek shade or shelter in the (bookable) straw-roofed heated cabana on the front terrace. To totally unwind, enjoy a relaxing overnight stay in one of the stylish, modern guest rooms set around the garden.

Chef **Simon Lawrence**. 3 course lunch from **£25**. 3 course dinner from **£30**. Seats **60**. Bedrooms **15**. Room rate from **£69**

88 Main Road, Littleton, Winchester, SO22 6QS
01962 880218
www.runninghorseinn.co.uk

f The Running Horse Inn
🐦 @runninghorseinn
📷 @therunninghorseinn

59 Ⓢ

CHEWTON GLEN HOTEL

Explore the extensive grounds, gawp at the exceptional spa and poke your head into James Martin's on-site cookery school at this idyll of utter luxury.

The Dining Room encapsulates the hotel's quintessentially English vibe with a touch of cosmopolitan. Offering a nexus of conservatories, intimate spaces and an open wine room, casual and formal dining options are available.

Produce from the kitchen garden is used in intelligently created and impeccably plated creations.

Chef **Luke Matthews**. 3 course lunch from **£26.50**. 3 course dinner from **£51**. Seats **180**. Bedrooms **72**. Room rate from **£370**

New Forest, Hampshire, BH25 6QS
01425 282212
www.chewtonglen.com

f Chewton Glen Hotel & Spa
🐦 @chewtonglen
📷 @chewtonglen

60 Ⓢ

THE FONTMELL

Such is the commitment to local fodder at this much-loved Dorset inn that the team have started breeding their own Gloucester Old Spot/Berkshire pigs two miles from the pub.

Game, meat, fish and vegetables that land in head chef Tom Shaw's kitchen are sourced with a similar emphasis on provenance, while the dishes served in the smart dining room or informal bar often take inspiration from afar. In summer, join the crowd thronging the garden for icy G&Ts and freshly made stone-baked pizzas.

Chef **Tom Shaw**. 3 course lunch from **£19**. 3 course dinner from **£28**. Seats **40**. Bedrooms **6**. Room rate from **£85**

Crown Hill, Fontmell Magna, Shaftesbury, Dorset, SP7 0PA
01747 811441
www.thefontmell.com

f The Fontmell
🐦 @thefontmell
📷 @thefontmell

61 ⑤
THE EASTBURY HOTEL

This Georgian townhouse hotel was recently acquired by top-drawer hoteliers Peter and Lana de Savary. And as part of its reinvigoration, the hotel will soon enjoy the addition of a new spa and extra bedrooms set within its walled gardens.

Esteemed regional producers play a starring role in the hotel's two AA rosette Seasons restaurant and in a seven course tasting menu served in the conservatory. Edible flowers, herbs and a chef's garden demonstrate the kitchen's dedication to keeping things fresh.

Chef **Matthew Street**. 3 course lunch from **£30**. 3 course dinner from **£40**. Seats **60**. Bedrooms **22**. Room rate from **£140**

Long Street, Sherborne, Dorset, DT9 3BY
01935 813131
www.theeastburyhotel.co.uk

f The Eastbury Hotel Sherborne Dorset
🐦 @eastbury_hotel
📷 @theeastbury

63
HIX OYSTER & FISH HOUSE

Pre-dinner snacks of Bigbury Bay cockle popcorn, scrumpy-fried River Yealm rock oysters and a glass of Furleigh Estate fizz set the scene for an evening at this ode to the sea in Dorset.

Phenomenally fresh fish and seafood dominate the menu at Mark Hix's Lyme Regis restaurant, where a network of West Country producers keeps the offering fabulously local. The roomy terrace provides plenty of space for lunchtime sunning in summer. And keep an eye open for Mark's Kitchen Table – an intimate lunchtime dining experience in the chef's Dorset home.

Chef **Ben Fuzzard**. 3 course lunch from **£23**. 3 course dinner from **£23**. Seats **45**

Cobb Road, Lyme Regis, Dorset, DT7 3JP
01297 446910
www.hixrestaurants.co.uk

f Hix Oyster and Fish House
🐦 @HIXRestaurants
📷 @hixrestaurants

62 ⑤
ACORN INN

This bucolic 16th century dining pub appeared in Thomas Hardy's *Tess of the d'Urbervilles*. Old beams, roaring fires, malt whiskies galore, an original skittle alley and ten elegant bedrooms are all part of its considerable historic charm.

The AA rosette restaurant prides itself on beautifully cooked dishes made with Dorset ingredients and, in summer, diners can eat in a convivial beer garden while exploring a refreshing array of real ales and ciders.

Chef **Robert Ndungu**. 3 course lunch from **£25**. 3 course dinner from **£25**. Seats **45**. Bedrooms **10**. Room rate from **£105**

28 Fore Street, Evershot, Dorset, DT2 0JW
01935 83 228
www.acorn-inn.co.uk

f The Acorn Inn
🐦 @Acorn_Inn
📷 @acorn_inn

Devon

Devon

Restaurants listed in the guide correspond to the numbers plotted on the map.

■ Higher member | ■ Member

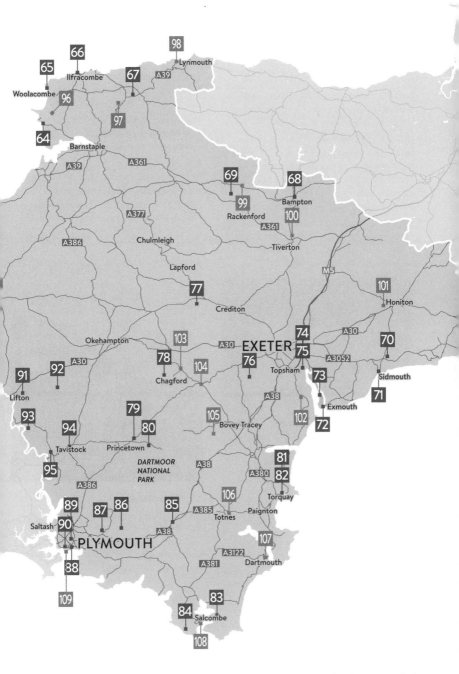

Locations are approximate.

64 Ⓢ

THE DINING ROOM AT SAUNTON

Coastal views to dine for

Since head chef Mathias Oberg took over the kitchen at Saunton a year ago, he's overseen the restaurant achieve two AA rosettes.

Having cooked at feted Michelin starred restaurants across the world, Mathias left the frenetic London restaurant scene to ply his cheffy trade overlooking one of the most stunning beaches in the UK.

Crowd pleasing brasserie-style menus (well-hung steaks and fresh fish cooked with aplomb) complement beautiful facilities that include a soon-to-be-launched spa and wellness experience at the four star hotel.

Chef **Mathias Oberg**
3 course lunch from **£28**
3 course dinner from **£32**
Seats **150**
Bedrooms **83**
Room rate from **£98**

Saunton, near Braunton, Devon, EX33 1LQ
01271 890212

www.sauntonsands.co.uk

f Saunton Sands Hotel
🐦 @sauntonsandshot
📷 @saunton_sandshotel

65 Ⓢ

WATERSMEET HOTEL

Boutique dining at the beach

With its sweeping views and private steps down to the beach, this attractive boutique hotel dazzles diners with its splendid coastal location.

Inside the charming seaside exterior, New England-style simplicity provides a restful ambience for contemplating ever-changing seascapes.

The stylish two AA rosette Pavilion restaurant, with its sea-facing windows, is the place to enjoy the skilful creations of head chef John Prince, while the bistro is popular for informal meals. On sunny days the outdoor pool is glorious, but for a spot of cosy pampering head to the indoor pool and spa.

Chef **John Prince**
3 course lunch from **£28**
3 course dinner from **£50**
Seats **55**
Bedrooms **28**
Room rate from **£155**

Woolacombe, Devon, EX34 7EB
01271 870333

www.watersmeethotel.co.uk

f Watersmeet Hotel
🐦 @watersmeethotel
📷 @watersmeetwoolacombe

THOMAS CARR @ THE OLIVE ROOM

Michelin star by the sea

The simple decor at this unassuming little restaurant on an Ilfracombe back street provides a blank canvas for Thomas Carr's one Michelin star cooking.

Encounter a delectable meeting of art and science – with a touch of quirky thrown in. Minimal descriptions on the menu hardly do justice to the creative masterpieces emerging from Carr's kitchen. Multi element, complicated cooking is the order of the day with an emphasis on local ingredients and ultra-fresh seafood landed just down the hill. Despite the culinary thrills, service is smiley and informal – yet well informed.

Chefs **Thomas Carr & John Cairns**
6 course tasting menu **£75**
Seats **16**

56 Fore Street, Ilfracombe, Devon, EX34 9DJ
01271 867831

www.thomascarrdining.co.uk

f Thomas Carr at The Olive Room
🐦 @thomascarrchef
📷 @thomascarrattheoliveroom

THE COACH HOUSE BY MICHAEL CAINES

Rural charm and glamour

Recently awarded a third AA rosette and Restaurant of the Year gold in the South West Tourism Awards, The Coach House by Michael Caines is one for gourmets seeking rural dining with a dash of glamour.

The smart dining space of the 17th century former coaching house, set in the grounds of luxurious Kentisbury Grange Hotel, blends rustic relaxation with contemporary decor.

On the cuisine front, head chef James Mason and his handpicked brigade of Caines-trained talent craft classic yet innovative dishes, designed to reflect seasonality and local produce.

Chef **James Mason**
3 course lunch from **£23.95**
3 course dinner from **£50**
Seats **50**
Bedrooms **16**
Room rate from **£110**

Kentisbury Grange Hotel, Kentisbury, Barnstaple, Devon, EX31 4NL
01271 882295

www.kentisburygrange.com

f Kentisbury Grange
🐦 @kentisburyg
📷 @kentisburygrange

WINNER
2018
TRENCHERMAN'S
AWARDS
BEST DINING PUB

68 Ⓢ

THE SWAN

One for the bucket list

It's been another successful year for Paul and Donna Berry at The Swan in Bampton, one of Devon's most decorated dining pubs.

Not only did the cheffing duo scoop top honours at the Devon Tourism Awards, Taste of the West Awards and make a considerable jump up the Estrella Top 50 Gastro Pub rankings, the inn was also awarded Trencherman's Best Dining Pub for a second time at the glamorous awards ceremony in November 2017 – a first in the awards' four year history.

Despite the gastronomic glory, the chef-patron pair haven't let the list of accolades go to their heads. Locally sourced dishes such as slow-cooked Exmoor lamb shank are excellent value, the daily menu continues to feature much-loved classics like steak and kidney suet pudding, and you'll still find a band of Bampton locals propping up the bar.

If you're making the trip – all this silverware is drawing the crowds – book one of the three cosy country bedrooms and look forward to a hearty English breakfast the next morning.

Chefs **Paul and Donna Berry**
3 course lunch from **£25**
3 course dinner from **£30**
Seats **60**
Bedrooms **3**
Room rate from **£90**

Station Road, Bampton,
Tiverton, Devon, EX16 9NG
01398 332248
www.theswan.co

f The Swan
🐦 @theswanbampton
📷 @theswanbampton

THE MASONS ARMS

Exmoor excellence

As ex head chef of The Waterside Inn at Bray and holder of a Michelin star here for 12 consecutive years, chef proprietor Mark Dodson has serious form.

A rural country pub – complete with charming ancient bar and bucolic views – is the setting for your seduction by Mark's classic flavour combinations and elegant execution. Dishes such as fillet of beef with daube, roasted carrots, potato puree and red wine jus feel just right when served with views of rolling farmland.

Mark's wife and business partner, Sarah Dodson, runs front of house like a well oiled machine. A three course lunch for £25 is exceptional value and don't miss the chance to grab a copy of Mark's recently published cookbook, *This is Mine*, when you visit.

Chefs **Mark Dodson & Jamie Coleman**
3 course lunch from **£25**
3 course dinner from **£47.50**
Seats **28**

Knowstone, South Molton, Devon, EX36 4RY
01398 341231

www.masonsarmsdevon.co.uk

f The Masons Arms Knowstone
🐦 @masonsknowstone
📷 @masonsarms_kitchen

THE SALTY MONK
RESTAURANT WITH ROOMS

Heavenly hub of classic cooking

The 16th century house may have waved goodbye to its salt-selling monks a long time ago, but it remains a top Devon destination for foodies seeking the holy trinity of beautiful cooking, fine wines and divine dining spaces.

Resident chef proprietor Andy Witheridge has held two AA rosettes for the last 15 years, and crafts classic dishes with a focus on locally sourced produce and 'real food'.

In addition to the à la carte offerings, gourmets make a pilgrimage for a heavenly afternoon tea which can be savoured in the award winning gardens or on the splendid patio.

Chef **Andy Witheridge**
3 course dinner from **£29.50**
Seats **35**
Bedrooms **7**
Room rate from **£135**

Church Street, Sidford, Sidmouth, Devon, EX10 9QP
01395 513174

www.saltymonk.com

f The Salty Monk
🐦 @thesaltymonk

71 [S]

THE RIVIERA HOTEL AND RESTAURANT
Traditional glamour

For grandeur by the sea and two AA rosette dining, head to Sidmouth's elegant Riviera Hotel on The Esplanade.

There's an impressive choice to be found on chef Martin Osedo's menus, and each dish is created with an attention to detail that's echoed throughout the hotel.

Run by the same family for more than 40 years, the generational theme extends to the menus with fish sourced from a third generation family fishing business. Enjoy cocktails in the Regency Bar or lunch on the terrace for the full Riviera-chic experience.

Chef **Martin Osedo**
2 course lunch from **£26**
3 course dinner from **£40**
Seats **80** restaurant, **60** terrace
Bedrooms **26**
Room rate from **£210**

The Esplanade, Sidmouth, Devon, EX10 8AY
01395 515201
www.hotelriviera.co.uk

72

SAVEUR
French with a twist

Since taking over the reins at Exmouth's Les Saveurs, Nigel Wright and Kerry Dow have rebranded the restaurant, bringing the classic French bistro stylishly up to date.

Fine-dining-loving francophiles needn't fear though; this new lease of life is less an overhaul and more a palate-extending development.

The couple bring a breadth of experience: Nigel trained under Michael Womersley (formerly of Le Manoir and Claridges) and crafts dishes such as crispy panko cod cheeks, and roasted monkfish with celeriac puree and bourguignon sauce. Look out for the cracking British cheese trolley, too.

Chef **Nigel Wright**
3 course lunch from **£19**
3 course dinner from **£30**
Seats **32**

9 Tower Street, Exmouth, Devon, EX8 1NT
01395 269459
www.saveursrestaurant.com

f Saveur Restaurant
@ @saveurexmouth

WINNER
2018
TRENCHERMAN'S
AWARDS
AWARD FOR CREATIVITY
AND INNOVATION

73 Ⓢ
LYMPSTONE MANOR
Realisation of a dream

Set in an outstanding position with views across the wildlife-rich Exe estuary, Lympstone Manor is the realisation of a lifelong dream by acclaimed chef Michael Caines.

This is Caines' vision of exquisite country house hospitality with plenty of romance thrown in. He wanted to create 'Cinderella moments', a chance to escape the outside world through secluded luxury.

Exclusivity pervades the building and is reflected in every detail, from the commissioned artwork and outdoor soak tubs to the fine food which has already achieved a Michelin star.

Three unique dining rooms are the setting for lunch and dinner, with options including a three course lunch menu, an à la carte seafood tasting menu and Michael's signature eight course tasting menu. Wine is a particular passion for Caines: his world class cellar now has more than 600 bins and he's just planted a vineyard in the 28 acres. Keep an eye out for special wine events and dinners.

Chef **Michael Caines**
3 course lunch from **£60**
3 course dinner from **£125**
Seats **60**
Bedrooms **21**
Room rate from **£315**

Courtlands Lane,
Exmouth, Devon, EX8 3NZ
01395 202040
www.lympstonemanor.co.uk

f Lympstone Manor
🐦 @lympstone_manor
📷 @lympstone_manor

Photos: David Griffen

THE SALUTATION INN

Sumptuous dining in historic Topsham

This charming 18th century restaurant with rooms is set in one of the prettiest towns in Devon, and delights foodies with modern British cooking with a French kick.

Talented chef Tom Williams-Hawkes creates weekly-changing menus celebrating fish fresh from the River Exe, along with a cornucopia of tasty crops and cuts from the Devon countryside. Tom, who learned his trade with Michael Caines (Gidleigh and Abode Exeter), has the sumptuous cooking covered while his wife Amelia looks after the guests. Enjoy lunch in the airy GlassHouse atrium or sip aperitifs in one of two comfortable sitting rooms before feasting in the attractive restaurant or private dining room.

Chef **Tom Williams-Hawkes**
3 course lunch from **£25**
4 course dinner from **£42.50**
6 course dinner from **£68.50**
Seats **28**
Bedrooms **6**
Room rate from **£135**

68 Fore Street, Topsham, Devon, EX3 0HL
01392 873060

www.salutationtopsham.co.uk

f Salutation Inn
🐦 @salutation1
📷 @salutationinn

THE GALLEY RESTAURANT

Fabulous fish on the Exe

Fish and seafood get the starring role at this intimate restaurant by Topsham quay. Top-notch ingredients from the Devon countryside and dazzlingly fresh fish shine in dishes which are artful in their simplicity.

Well-executed cooking from chef Lee Harry, plus superb service from owner Nigel Mitchell and team, explains why this bijou gem scores highly with both locals and visiting gourmets.

By night, The Galley takes on the vibe of a private dining club: Nigel works the tables with consummate skill, matching great food and fine wines with charm and aplomb.

By day, the purse-pleasing set lunches are worth making the trip for.

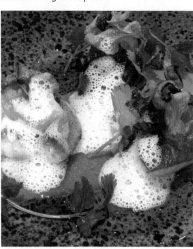

Chef **Lee Harry**
3 course lunch from **£22.50**
3 course dinner from **£31.50**
Seats **48**

41 Fore Street, Topsham, Devon, EX3 0HU
01392 876078

www.galleyrestaurant.co.uk

f The Galley Restaurant Topsham
🐦 @galleytopsham

THE NOBODY INN

Whisky galore at a rural dining pub

Hidden away in countryside between the Haldon Hills and Teign Valley lies the 17th century NoBody Inn. All blackened beams, tobacco-stained walls and antique furniture, this four AA star pub (and winner of *The Good Hotel Guide* Inn of the Year 2017) bewitches with its log fire, pretty country garden and comfortably quirky bedrooms.

As befits last year's winner of Trencherman's Best Bar List, it stocks over 250 whiskies, an extensive wine list and a killer house gin. Pair well-crafted drinks with deliciously authentic dining pub dishes made with ingredients such as local game and River Teign mussels.

Chef **Michael Pooley**
3 course lunch from **£24**
3 course dinner from **£30**
Seats **50**
Bedrooms **5**
Room rate from **£99**

Doddiscombsleigh, Exeter, Devon, EX6 7PS
01647 252394

www.nobodyinn.co.uk

f The NoBody Inn
🐦 @thenobodyinn
📷 @thenobodyinn

PASCHOE HOUSE

Fresh for 2018

There aren't many country house hotels of this calibre where you can take your pooch along for the weekend, let alone where they offer to look after it for you.

But with the Two Moors Way footpath on the doorstep and being just a short drive from Dartmoor, this is a luxurious spot from which to explore striking countryside with a four-legged pal in tow.

After a day's adventuring, reward yourself with a sumptuous supper at the Grade II-listed manor's restaurant. Abode Exeter's former pastry chef Samuel Brook is the new head chef and crafts an exquisite collection of fine dining dishes.

Other distractions include a stuffed ostrich in the bar and delectable cocktails.

Chef **Samuel Brook**
3 course lunch from **£35**
3 course dinner from **£60**
Seats **24**
Bedrooms **9**
Room rate from **£220**

Bow, Crediton, Devon, EX17 6JT
01363 84244

www.paschoehouse.co.uk

f Paschoe House
🐦 @paschoehouse
📷 @paschoehouse

78 [S]
GIDLEIGH PARK
New era at the Dartmoor manor

The arrival of executive head chef Chris Simpson (who has taken over from Trencherman's Best Chef 2018 winner Michael Wignall) heralds a new chapter in the significant gastronomic history of Gidleigh Park.

As former head chef at two Michelin starred Restaurant Nathan Outlaw in Cornwall, Chris' culinary clout is a great match for the Tudor-style country house. Exceptional seasonal ingredients benefit from his classical cooking style and flair for imbuing time-honoured dishes with a modern twist. Pair that with Gidleigh's impressive cellar – one of the best in the UK – for a seriously good dining experience.

By the meandering waters of the River Teign, Gidleigh enjoys a spectacular location on the edge of Dartmoor National Park, while its Arts and Crafts interiors (beautifully curated by the Brownsword family) add tranquility and romance.

Chef **Chris Simpson**
3 course lunch from **£65**
3 course dinner from **£125**
Seats **50**
Bedrooms **24**
Room rate from **£275**

Chagford, Devon, TQ13 8HH
01647 432367
www.gidleigh.co.uk

f Gidleigh Park
🐦 @gidleighhotel
📷 @brownswordhotels

79 ⑤
TWO BRIDGES HOTEL
Dartmoor dining delights

Nestled between two bridges in the heart of the rolling moors, this timeless hotel and restaurant is both a cosy haven for fireside sipping in winter and a summer spot in which to sample locally brewed ales in river-view gardens.

Whatever time of year you choose to visit, executive chef Mike Palmer's menus are brimming with locally sourced produce in beautifully executed dishes. The oak-panelled dining room sets the scene for an exquisite tasting menu experience, while the relaxed bar – complete with crackling log fires and original antiques – houses a hearty bill of British classics.

Follow lunch with a turn around the tors before returning to sample a seriously good Devon cream tea.

Chef **Mike Palmer**
3 course lunch from **£22**
3 course dinner from **£49**
Seats **60**
Bedrooms **32**
Room rate from **£99**

Two Bridges, Dartmoor, Devon, PL20 6SW
01822 892300

www.twobridges.co.uk

f Two Bridges Hotel
🐦 @two_bridges
📷 @two_bridges_hotel

80 ⑤
PRINCE HALL
Charm and tranquility

The magic of Dartmoor is captured in this charming, family-run boutique country house, which offers a getaway with intimate dining, glorious gardens, roaring log fires and characterful accommodation.

Luke Daly treats guests to seasonally changing dishes using ingredients that are home grown, home reared or scrupulously locally sourced. The warm atmosphere welcomes casual daytime diners, alfresco eaters and special occasion-seekers. The invite also extends to four legged friends, making this open-all-year spot the perfect launch pad from which to pursue moorland adventures.

Chef **Luke Daly**
3 course lunch from **£25**
3 course dinner from **£35**
Seats **28**
Bedrooms **9**
Room rate from **£99**

Dunnabridge Road, Princetown, Devon, PL20 6SA
01822 890403

www.princehall.co.uk

f Prince Hall Hotel & Restaurant
🐦 @princehallhotel
📷 @princehallhotel

81 ⑤

JOHN BURTON-RACE HOTEL & RESTAURANT

Clever cooking with French flair

Long synonymous with Michelin starred restaurants, John Burton-Race's moniker certifies creative, clever cooking at this Torquay hotel and restaurant.

Whatever style of sustenance you're craving (choose from à la carte, taster or bistro menus), you'll enjoy dishes inspired by the chef's Channel 4 series *French Leave*. Those wanting to push the boat out should opt for the six course tasting menu matched with classic and new world wines. Expect excellent service and fine dining at a fraction of London prices.

Chef **John Burton-Race**
3 course lunch from **£19.50**
3 course dinner from **£19.95**
Seats **63**
Bedrooms **47**
Room rate from **£79**

Belgrave Road, Torquay, Devon, TQ2 5HG
08006 895415

www.johnburtonracerestaurant.co.uk

f John Burton-Race Hotel & Restaurant
🐦 @jbrrestaurant
📷 @jbrrestaurant

82

THE ORANGE TREE RESTAURANT

Hidden treasure

Classical cooking awaits at this gem of a restaurant that's tucked away in a quiet street just a pebble's skim from Torquay harbour.

This year husband and wife team Bernd and Sharon Wolf celebrate a decade of serving British and European dishes against a backdrop of crisp white linen and candlelight.

The pair's passion for the countryside's rich pickings, an attractive wine list and friendly service have garnered this little restaurant a loyal following. Everything from bread to chutney is crafted in house and there's an emphasis on regional produce. For special occasions the seven course tasting menu is exemplary.

Chef **Bernd Wolf**
3 course dinner from **£29**
Seats **42**

14-16 Parkhill Road, Torquay,
Devon, TQ1 2AL
01803 213936

www.orangetreerestaurant.co.uk

f The Orange Tree Restaurant
🐦 @orangetreerest
📷 @orangetreetorquay

83 ⓢ

THE MILLBROOK INN

French–Brit fusion

Head to south Devon's The Millbrook Inn for a fine dining fusion fix on the sunny courtyard.

Honouring both his Gallic roots and the lush surroundings of the 16th century inn, head chef Jean-Phillipe Bidart's menus feature British dishes with infusions of French influence.

Boaty types can moor at the pontoon (which is gratifyingly nearby as the restaurant enjoys a creek-side spot) when they cruise by for lunch or dinner. The lengthy wine and real ale lists are pretty impressive, so make sure that someone else is in charge of the craft. But if all else fails, there's always the spacious Loft Suite upstairs for overnight stays with a private balcony and water views.

Chef **JP Bidart**
3 course lunch from **£15**
3 course dinner from **£25**
Seats **45**
Bedrooms **1**
Room rate from **£150**

South Pool, near Kingsbridge, Devon, TQ7 2RW
01548 531581

www.millbrookinnsouthpool.co.uk

f Millbrook Inn
🐦 @southpoolducks
📷 @millbrookinnsouthpool

84 ⓢ

SOAR MILL COVE HOTEL

The great escape

In an Area of Outstanding Natural Beauty and hugging the hillside above stylish Salcombe, this family and dog-friendly hotel provides a great escape. Choose from secluded suites for couples, flexible family rooms or one of the three self-catering properties.

Two AA rosette fine dining comes courtesy of chef Ian MacDonald and team, and showcases meat and seafood from the nearby pastures and shore. It's also a great location from which to explore the scenic South Hams or work up an appetite along the South West Coast Path.

Alternatively, wallow in the spa and spring-fed indoor pool or try the mini-gym and games chalet.

Chef **Ian MacDonald**
3 course lunch from **£33**
3 course dinner from **£39**
Seats **60**
Bedrooms **22**
Room rate from **£199**

Marlborough, Salcombe, Devon, TQ7 3DS
01548 561566

www.soarmillcove.co.uk

f Soar Mill Cove Hotel
🐦 @soarmillcove
📷 @soarmillcovehotel

85 Ⓢ

GLAZEBROOK HOUSE HOTEL

Quirky glamour on Dartmoor

With nine distinctively designed bedrooms and a menu dictated by the seasons, no two trips to this eccentric boutique hotel will be the same.

Whether you plump for the White Rabbit double, with its playing card motif and sheepskin bed, or the Mad Hatter suite with free-standing tub and tartan galore, you'll have stacks of material for your Instagram feed.

Dining in the restaurant at Glazebrook is an equally awesome experience. Produce is sourced from pastures within 50 miles of the hotel and fashioned into picture-worthy breakfast, lunch and dinner plates by head chef Josh Ackland.

While light lunches of beetroot and blue cheese risotto and suppers such as white wine battered fish and chips hint at chef's whimsical ways, the six course tasting menu provides a fairytale experience.

Chef **Josh Ackland**
3 course lunch from **£20**
3 course dinner from **£35**
Seats **64**
Bedrooms **9**
Room rate from **£149**

South Brent, Devon, TQ10 9JE
01364 73322
www.glazebrookhouse.com

f Glazebrook House Hotel
🐦 @glazebrookhouse
📷 @glazebrookhouse

86 Ⓐ
THE TREBY ARMS
Rustic dining pub

At The Treby you can turn up in chinos and blazer or feel equally comfortable in your wellies. This rustic country pub in the village of Sparkwell welcomes everyone from couples to families – even your pooch will be treated as a guest in the bar.

A change in direction sees the pub embracing a more casual and contemporary approach to fine dining. Tasting menus have been replaced by pub classics and grills – albeit with a fabulous Treby twist. Varied menus focusing on quality produce have been devised to appeal to different budgets and appetites, and are served in a relaxed atmosphere.

Chef **Fletcher Andrews**
3 course lunch from **£20**
3 course dinner from **£30**
Seats **65**

Sparkwell, Plympton, Devon, PL7 5DD
01752 837363

www.thetrebyarms.co.uk

f Treby Arms
🐦 @thetrebyarms
📷 @thetrebyarms

87 Ⓢ
BORINGDON HALL
Grandeur and gourmandizing

For a thoroughly indulgent Devon dine and stay experience, the historic grandeur and culinary class of Boringdon Hall is fabulous. Head chef Scott Paton has been collecting accolades – including a third AA rosette in 2017 – since he brought his refined, seasonal cookery to the Gallery Restaurant in 2016.

Don a dashing dress or blazer and dine on elegant and innovative tasting menus. The 40 finely refurbished bedrooms offer the opportunity for full exploration of the inspired wine pairings, too. A self-indulgent retreat at the Elizabethan manor house isn't complete without a couple of hours unwinding on the massage table and lounging by the plunge pool in the sumptuous Gaia Spa.

Chef **Scott Paton**
3 course lunch from **£29.50**
3 course dinner from **£55**
Seats **54**
Bedrooms **40**
Room rate from **£159**

Boringdon Hill, Plymouth, Devon, PL7 4DP
01752 545795

www.boringdonhall.co.uk

f Boringdon Hall Hotel
🐦 @boringdonhall
📷 @boringdonhall

88
BARBICAN KITCHEN
Dine at the Distillery

The Tanner brothers' contemporary brasserie within the Plymouth Gin Distillery has been going strong for over a decade. With a swoonsome selection of Anglo and Asian-inspired eats and eye-popping interiors, it's no surprise that the colourful space remains popular.

Plymouth dayboats and Philip Warren Butchers continue to stock the modern menu with seasonal catches and steaks destined for the Big Green Egg ceramic grill. Vegetarians and vegans are well served too, with produce from the West Country adopting lead roles in creative combinations such as harissa glazed barbecue aubergine with cous cous, yogurt and pistachio dukkah. For parties, book the stunning private dining room which can accommodate 22 guests.

Chefs **Chris & James Tanner, Martyn Compton**
3 course lunch from **£17.95**
3 course dinner from **£17.95**
Seats **100**

Plymouth Gin Distillery,
60 Southside Street, Plymouth, PL1 2LQ
01752 604448

www.barbicankitchen.com

f Barbican Kitchen
🐦 @barbicankitchen
📷 @barbicankitchen

89
THE GREEDY GOOSE
Modern dining in a historical setting

Since opening The Greedy Goose in 2014, chef patron Ben Palmer and his wife Francesca have aimed to create their vision of a perfect restaurant: serving food they love to eat in a characterful environment.

With years of high-end cooking experience and an appreciation of seasonal eating which goes back to childhood (his father was a gamekeeper), Ben creates modern dishes which are packed full of flavour, made with quality ingredients sourced locally.

Francesca heads up the front of house team and creates a friendly atmosphere in this extraordinary setting: Prysten House is the oldest building in historic Plymouth.

Chefs **Ben Palmer & Tom Dodd**
3 course lunch from **£20**
3 course dinner from **£20**
Seats **75**

Prysten House, Finewell Street, Plymouth, Devon, PL1 2AE
01752 252001

www.thegreedygoose.co.uk

f The Greedy Goose
🐦 @greedygooseplym
📷 @greedygooseplym

90

ROCK SALT CAFE
Funky fusion food

Laid-back brunch vibes meet impressive South West fine dining at this family-run restaurant in the heart of Plymouth.

Not only do chef patron Dave Jenkins and his right hand man Joe Turner produce an all-day line-up of next level brunch plates – think hog mac 'n' cheese with thyme-roasted mushrooms or baked green eggs with pesto and gruyère – the duo also craft award winning tasting menus after dark.

Expect a marriage of South-east Asian flavours and hearty British (read 'local') fare in inventive combinations such as miso black cod with Thai rice, choy sum and roasted seaweed.

Chefs **Dave Jenkins & Joe Turner**
3 course lunch from **£18**
3 course dinner from **£25**
Seats **70**

31 Stonehouse Street, Plymouth,
Devon, PL1 3PE
01752 225522

www.rocksaltcafe.co.uk

f Rock Salt Cafe Brasserie
🐦 @rocksaltcafeuk
📷 @rocksaltcafe

91 Ⓢ

THE ARUNDELL ARMS HOTEL & RESTAURANT
Reeling in the foodies

Round off a day casting a line at this country hotel's fly fishing school with a glass of bubbly and an exquisite dinner in the glittering chandeliered dining room.

The restaurant is an elegant setting and has held two AA rosettes since 1987. And for the past ten years the sumptuous à la carte and five course seasonal tasting menus have been in the capable hands of head chef Steve Pidgeon.

Finish with a nightcap by the drawing room fire before you repose in a comfy country-themed bedroom, ready for another day of rural recreation in the wilds of Dartmoor.

Chef **Steven Pidgeon**
3 course lunch from **£23**
3 course dinner from **£49.50**
Seats **60**
Bedrooms **26**
Room rate from **£160**

Fore Street, Lifton, Devon, PL16 0AA
01566 784666

www.arundellarms.com

f The Arundell Arms Hotel
🐦 @thearundellarms
📷 @arundellarmsfishing

92 ⓢ
LEWTRENCHARD MANOR

Dine at the Jacobean manor

This Jacobean manor house, rich in history and stuffed full of intriguing wood-panelled rooms, coats of arms and ancient fireplaces, provides a characterful setting for head chef Matthew Peryer's West Country-inspired cooking.

Every manor house should have a walled garden and Lewtrenchard's impressive offering is fully utilised by the chef, who works closely with head gardener Martin Ashley to ensure a crop of unusual and often-changing varieties of vegetables and fruits each season.

On dry days, visitors are invited to explore the various gardens within the grounds before lunch or afternoon tea in the sunny Italianate courtyard.

History pervades the dining room and, despite some pretty stern portraits on the walls, a friendly front of house team create a relaxed atmosphere. If you want to dine in more informal surrounds, try the bar which provides snacks such as a cracking venison burger and plate of local cheeses with chutney.

Chef **Matthew Peryer**
3 course lunch
from **£25.50**
3 course dinner
from **£45.50**
Seats **40**
Bedrooms **14**
Room rate from **£180**

Lewdown, Okehampton,
Devon, EX20 4PN
01566 783222

www.lewtrenchard.co.uk

f Lewtrenchard Manor
𝕐 @lewtrenchard
◎ @lewtrenchardmanor

HOTEL ENDSLEIGH

Epicurean escapism

The Grade I-listed hunting and fishing lodge has been one of Devon's dreamiest country house destinations since the Polizzi family took it over more than a decade ago. Surrounded by woodland and award winning gardens, the Duke of Bedford's former residence now houses a refined restaurant and lounge, 18 elegantly furnished bedrooms and two contemporary suites in converted stables.

Despite Italian roots, head chef Jose Graziosi draws on his experience in the South West to craft innovative fine dining dishes showcasing the Cornish catch and Devon pastures. The wine list further celebrates this glorious pocket of the country, with notable finds from regional vineyards such as Sharpham.

Chef **Jose Graziosi**
3 course lunch from **£30**
3 course dinner from **£47**
Seats **40**
Bedrooms **18**
Room rate from **£200**

Milton Abbot, Tavistock, Devon, PL19 0PQ
01822 870000

www.hotelendsleigh.com

f Hotel Endsleigh
🐦 @hotelendsleigh
📷 @hotelendsleigh

CHEF'S TIP

Thomas Carr, head chef, Thomas Carr @ The Olive Room (No 66)

'I really want to get back to the Pyne Arms (No 97).

I tried Ellis' Sunday lunch last year — now I need to sample the main menu.'

94
THE CORNISH ARMS
Unpretentious and award winning

So-called because it was the last coaching inn before Cornwall, this thriving Dartmoor pub is somewhere owners John and Emma Hooker profess they would *'love to visit themselves'*. A welcoming ethos, coupled with no-fuss dishes full of flavour and local produce, gives The Cornish Arms an accessible-to-all atmosphere.

There's no scrimping on quality though. John (Trencherman's Best Chef 2016) crafts classic combos that have seen the pub land a Michelin Bib Gourmand and, since 2013, inclusion in the Top 50 Gastro Pubs in the UK (it's currently at 21).

With an attractive beer garden, it's also a good spot for dining alfresco on sunny days.

Chef **John Hooker**
3 course lunch from **£19.50**
3 course dinner from **£25**
Seats **50**

15 West Street, Tavistock, Devon, PL19 8AN
01822 612145

www.thecornisharmstavistock.co.uk

f Cornish Arms
🐦 @cornisharmstavy
📷 @the_cornish_arms_tavistock

95 Ⓢ
THE HORN OF PLENTY
Utter comfort on Dartmoor

Located on the Devon/Cornwall border, this four star, independently-owned country house hotel oozes quality, tranquility and utter comfort. As its name suggests, it's the place to indulge in the nourishing spoils of nature.

Head chef Ashley Wright's two AA rosette dishes combine creativity, flavour and visual appeal, harnessing seasonal ingredients like Bocaddon Farm veal and Brixham red gurnard to great effect. Each carefully crafted plate is served against a stunning backdrop of the beautiful Tamar Valley, which can be enjoyed further with an overnight stay in one of the country-chic rooms.

Chef **Ashley Wright**
3 course lunch from **£24.50**
3 course dinner from **£49.50**
Seats **40**
Bedrooms **16**
Room rate from **£120**

Gulworthy, Tavistock, Devon, PL19 8JD
01822 832528

www.thehornofplenty.co.uk

f The Horn of Plenty Country House Hotel & Restaurant
🐦 @hornofplenty1
📷 @the_hornofplenty

TAKE 5

Coastal dining

148 Fistral Beach Hotel and Spa

Sensational suppers await at Fistral Beach for surfers and coastal wanderers. The hotel's Dune Restaurant serves up some of the freshest seafood caught on Cornish shores at this chilled-out spot.

158 Porthgwidden Beach Cafe

Sandy-toed alfresco dining is the order of the day for beach bums and seafood devotees. The local catch from St Ives, Looe and Mevagissey is crafted into Asian and Mediterranean-style dishes.

139 Porthminster Beach Cafe

Enjoy a bountiful offering of Asian-inspired seafood dishes at the much loved St Ives beach cafe. Gaze upon shimmering sands and glittering seas as you chow down on a platter piled high with the local catch.

65 Watersmeet Hotel

This charming boutique hotel, overlooking one of the UK's best beaches, embodies the spirit of great British seaside holidays – with the added benefit of stylish dining at the two AA rosette Pavilion restaurant.

55 The Crab House Cafe

Expect unfussy modern dining and the freshest seafood. Feast on plump Portland oysters, picked straight from the cafe's own beds, which arrive at your table within minutes of leaving the water.

More Devon

96
THE ROCK INN

Expect hugely appealing food which is as local as it gets at this 17th century village pub on the north Devon coast.

Menus demonstrate a modern approach to pub faves with international influences and dishes to suit all tastes – from deli boards to curries. Ingredients are sourced very close to home, such as Arlington lamb, Lee Bay crab, venison from Spreacombe and even own-reared rare-breed pork. Just as much attention is paid to the drinks list: five Cask Marque real ales, local ciders and an extensive wine list keep punters happy.

Visitors can choose to dine in the cosy, fire-lit bar or chill in the leafy conservatory.

Chef **Dominic Newman**. 3 course lunch from **£15**. 3 course dinner from **£20**. Seats **80**

Rock Hill, Georgeham, Devon, EX33 1JW
01271 890322
www.therockinn.biz

f Rock Inn
@ @therockinngeorgeham

97 Ⓢ
PYNE ARMS

Tucked away in a tiny hamlet in the lush north Devon hills, this traditional country pub offers warm hospitality and a menu of hearty classics. Owner chef Ellis Pannell and front of house manager Amie (husband and wife) serve traditional pub food with a twist, placing emphasis on exceptional local ingredients.

Real ale fans flock here, enticed by the many guest brews on the go, while those exploring the wild beauty of nearby Exmoor National Park and the north Devon coast can book one of three recently renovated ensuite rooms.

Chef **Ellis Pannell**. 3 course lunch from **£18**. 3 course dinner from **£28**. Seats **40**. Bedrooms **3**. Room rate from **£75**

East Down, Barnstaple, Devon, EX31 4LX
01271 850055
www.pynearms.co.uk

f Pyne Arms
🐦 @pynearms
@ @pynearms

98 Ⓢ
RISING SUN

Just a few steps from the sea, this 14th century dining pub is a landmark feature of dramatic Lynmouth.

Cosy up inside with dinner and drinks and watch the comings and goings in the harbour.

Chef Matthew Rutter makes full use of produce from the coast and nearby moorland, creating seasonal dishes with international influences, so alongside a classic ribeye from Exmoor you'll find the likes of monkfish roasted in ras el hanout, and sweet potato tagine.

Chef **Matthew Rutter**. 3 course lunch from **£27**. 3 course dinner from **£41.50**. Seats **20**. Bedrooms **14**. Room rate from **£135**

Harbourside, Lynmouth, Devon, EX35 6EG
01598 753223
www.risingsunlynmouth.co.uk

f The Rising Sun Hotel
🐦 @risingsunexmoor
📷 @risingsunlynmouth

99 Ⓢ
THE JUBILEE INN

Refurbishment has transformed The Jubilee into a comfortable private country home dining experience, complete with vintage wallpaper, leather furniture and eclectic personal touches from the family. Together, they've helped earn it two Taste of the West gold awards and a *Sunday Times* rating as one of the '*best places to eat, drink and stay*'.

Moorland exploration is rewarded with generous plates of wholesome honest fare with a dash of "what granny used to make". Stay in one of the family's seasonal boutique bedrooms to feel truly at home.

Chef **The Elliott family**. 3 course lunch from **£22**. 3 course dinner from **£22**. Seats **60**. Bedrooms **6**. Room rate from **£65**

West Anstey, South Molton, Devon, EX36 3PH
01398 341401
www.thejubileeinn.co.uk

f The Jubilee Inn
🐦 @Jubilee_Inn
📷 @thejubileeinn

100 Ⓢ
HARTNOLL HOTEL

Devon diners seeking a locally focused menu featuring the likes of West Coast scallops, Creedy Carver duck and West Country steaks, complemented by the finest wines (handpicked by the house sommelier), have long escaped to award winning Hartnoll.

For those seeking an edible experience of the sweet-toothed kind, cake-based refuge can be found in an impeccable assortment of handmade fancies, scones and sarnies. Take tea in the conservatory which overlooks landscaped gardens on the edge of Exmoor.

Chef **Paul Webber**. 3 course lunch from **£22**. 3 course dinner from **£30**. Seats **100**. Bedrooms **25**. Room rate from **£100**

Bolham, Tiverton, Devon, EX16 7RA
01884 252777
www.hartnollhotel.co.uk

f Hartnoll Hotel
🐦 @hartnollhotel
📷 @hartnollhoteldevon

101 Ⓢ
DEER PARK COUNTRY HOUSE

This Georgian country house is set in 80 acres of glorious Devon countryside and includes three miles of fly fishing on the River Otter. Take your pick from the four AA star, rustic chic guest rooms in the main house, the garden wing or even a luxury thatched treehouse, then kick back with an in-room pampering massage. Savour splendid views and creative cuisine in the two AA rosette restaurant, Loxton's. The menu changes daily and aims to include produce from the restored two acre walled garden in every dish.

Chef **Hadleigh Barrett**. 3 course lunch from **£21.50**. 3 course dinner from **£40**. Seats **35**. Bedrooms **33**. Room rate from **£110**

Weston, Honiton, Devon, EX14 3PG
01404 41266
www.deerparkcountryhotel.co.uk

f Deer Park Country House Hotel
🐦 @DeerParkHotel
📷 @deerparkcountryhouse

No 101
DEER PARK
COUNTRY HOUSE

102
RODEAN RESTAURANT

Situated on the village green, family-run Rodean Restaurant has been feeding the folk of Kenton and visitors to nearby Powderham Castle for almost twenty years. Chef patron Matthew Tilt draws on classic British and modern Mediterranean influences to fashion a menu stocked by Devon suppliers at this former butcher's shop.

Sample the experienced chef's full repertoire of refined dishes via the reasonably priced tasting menu or book a spot at one of the regular food and wine evenings.

Chef **Matthew Tilt**. 3 course lunch from **£24**. 3 course dinner from **£24**. Seats **36**

The Triangle, Kenton, Exeter, Devon, EX6 8LS
01626 890195
www.rodeanrestaurant.co.uk

f Rodean Restaurant
🐦 @Rodean_kenton
📷 @rodean_restaurant

104
THE HORSE

In the pretty Dartmoor town of Moretonhampstead, this friendly dining pub is full of foodie surprises such as a tapas menu which includes homemade bresaola and smoked-on-the-premises scallops.

For mains, the chargrilled 21-day hung Dartmoor ribeye steak and tempura battered hake with homemade tartare sauce will please discerning palates, while thin crust pizzas from the custom-built oven receive rave reviews. There's a small sunny courtyard for dining outside and the bar is a buzzy community hub with leather sofas, a roaring fire and regular live music events.

Chef **Nigel Hoyle**. 3 course lunch from **£20**. 3 course dinner from **£25**. Seats **60**

7 George Street, Moretonhampstead, Devon, TQ13 8PG
01647 440242
www.thehorsedartmoor.co.uk

f The Horse [Moretonhampstead, UK]
🐦 @horsedartmoor

103 ⬚
MILL END HOTEL

Days exploring the wilds of Dartmoor are extra special when they end at Mill End Hotel.

After traversing the ancient trails, take a fireside snooze or indulge in a tantalising afternoon tea that's freshly made each day. Then retreat to one of the country-style bedrooms to glam up for supper.

Excelling in classic British cookery, head chef Darren Knockton rewards weary walkers with expertly-presented dishes such as butter-roasted monkfish loin with spiced lentils, and poached asparagus with pickled morels and cured egg.

Chef **Darren Knockton**. 3 course lunch from **£24.50**. 3 course dinner from **£37**. Seats **40**. Bedrooms **21**. Room rate from **£150**

Dartmoor National Park, Chagford, Devon, TQ13 8JN
01647 432282
www.millendhotel.com

f Mill End Hotel
🐦 @millenddevon

105 ⬚
ILSINGTON COUNTRY HOUSE AND SPA

This quintessentially English spot, with its two AA rosette restaurant, multi-award winning spa and sweeping views, is an idyll of fine dining and rejuvenation.

Head chef Mike O'Donnell has been at the helm since 1998 and crafts sumptuous dishes balancing traditional classics with modern English cooking. Raiding Dartmoor's larder is high on his agenda, with ingredients regularly foraged from the grounds and eggs collected from the hotel's flock of hens.

Chef **Mike O'Donnell**. 3 course lunch from **£24.50**. 3 course dinner from **£39.50**. Seats **50**. Bedrooms **25**. Room rate from **£135**

Ilsington Village, near Haytor, Newton Abbot, Devon, TQ13 9RR
01364 661452
www.ilsington.co.uk

f Ilsington Country House Hotel
🐦 @IlsingtonHotel
📷 @ilsingtonhotel

106 ⑤
THE ROYAL SEVEN STARS

In the centre of Totnes, this characterful 17th century coaching inn harbours a secret behind its traditional public house facade.

The stylish TQ9 restaurant, sleek cocktail bar and luxurious rooms give the award winning Royal Seven Stars a dash of glamour.

Indulge in a glass of crisp fizz before heading in to an intimate dinner of contemporary dishes featuring seasonal, local ingredients – think Exmouth mussels, herb crusted lamb and Brixham's catch of the day. Or simply enjoy a coffee in the Saloon Bar and watch the world go by.

Chef **Dan Archer.** 3 course lunch from **£22.** 3 course dinner from **£27.** Seats **35.** Bedrooms **21.** Room rate from **£110**

The Plains, Totnes, Devon, TQ9 5DD
01803 862125
www.royalsevenstars.co.uk

f Royal Seven Stars Hotel
🐦 @rsstotnes
📷 @royalsevenstarshotel

107 ⑤
THE ROYAL
CASTLE HOTEL

With its Tudor fireplaces, spiral staircases and flagstone floors, this iconic 17th century building on Dartmouth's waterfront oozes character. The AA rosette Grill Room specialises in grass-fed British beef and is famed for its West Country aged fillet steaks, as well as dishes based around Devon delicacies and the daily catch. Downstairs, the oak-beamed Galleon Bar is a reliable bet for traditional home cooked meals or head to the contemporary Harbour Bar to catch up with friends over a light lunch.

Chef **Ankur Biswas.** 3 course lunch from **£25.** 3 course dinner from **£30.** Seats **60.** Bedrooms **24.** Room rate from **£140**

11 The Quay, Dartmouth, Devon, TQ6 9PS
01803 833033
www.royalcastle.co.uk

f The Royal Castle Hotel
🐦 @rchdartmouth1
📷 @rch_dartmouth_

108 ⑤
SALCOMBE HARBOUR
HOTEL & SPA

If you had views over Salcombe Estuary like the ones from almost every room at this swish spa hotel, you too would place a pair of binoculars and a (complimentary) drinks tray by the window.

The glam yachty vibe channelled in the 50 bedrooms and suites extends to the relaxed bar and Jetty Restaurant, where head chef Jamie Gulliford serves briny-fresh oysters, Devon crab and Salcombe Gin-cured salmon among other locally sourced lovelies.

Chef **Jamie Gulliford.** 3 course lunch from **£24.95.** 3 course dinner from **£29.95.** Seats **93.** Bedrooms **50.** Room rate from **£195**

Cliff Road, Salcombe, Devon, TQ8 8JH
01548 844444
www.salcombe-harbour-hotel.co.uk

f Salcombe Harbour Hotel & Spa
🐦 @salcombehotel
📷 @salcombeharbourhotel

109
THE FIG TREE @ 36

This family-run restaurant, close to Royal William Yard, is the kind of neighbourhood bistro everyone wishes was at the end of their street. Experienced chef Ryan Marsland creates internationally-inspired dishes using local and homegrown produce, while partner Tanya Poole greets guests with a home-from-home welcome in the small and relaxed dining space. A well priced menu, along with a focus on sustainability and community, makes this Plymouth newcomer as easy on the conscience as the bank balance.

Chef **Ryan Marsland.** 3 course lunch from **£18.** 3 course dinner from **£18.** Seats **40**

36 Admiralty Street, Plymouth, Devon, PL1 3RU
01752 253247
www.thefigtreeat36.co.uk

f The Fig Tree at 36
🐦 @FigTreeat36
📷 @thefigtreeat36

Cornwall

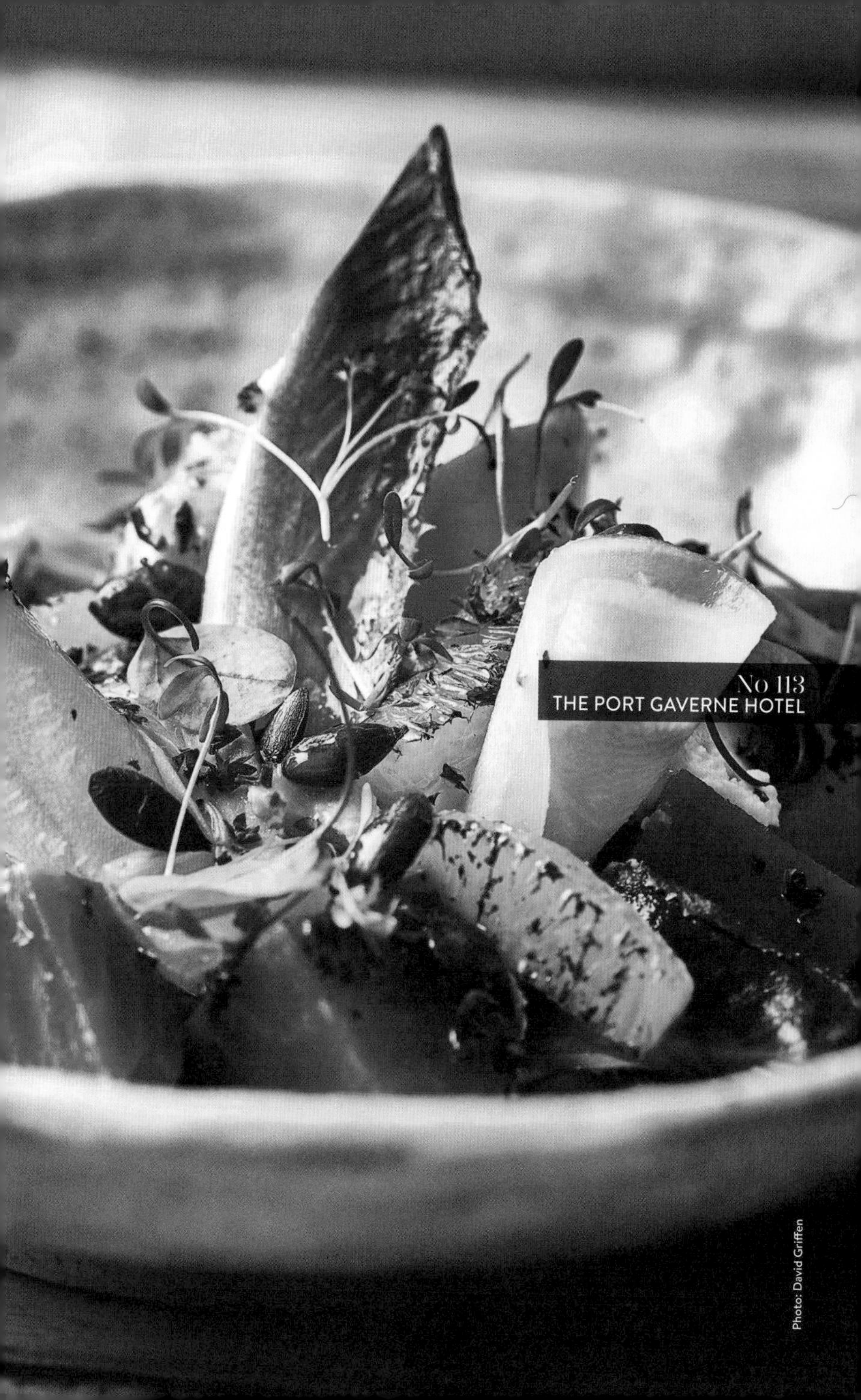

Photo: David Griffen

Cornwall

Restaurants listed in the guide correspond to the numbers plotted on the map.

■ Higher member | ■ Member

110 Langmans Restaurant
111 Talland Bay Hotel
112 The Old Quay House Hotel & Restaurant
113 The Port Gaverne Hotel
114 Restaurant Nathan Outlaw
115 Outlaw's Fish Kitchen
116 St Enodoc Hotel
117 The Mariners Public House
118 The Seafood Restaurant
119 St Petroc's Bistro
120 Rick Stein's Cafe
121 The Cornish Arms
122 Appleton's Bar & Restaurant
123 Jamie Oliver's Fifteen Cornwall
124 Tabb's Restaurant
125 The Lugger
126 The Nare Hotel
127 The Rosevine
128 The Idle Rocks
129 Hotel Tresanton
130 Oliver's
131 Star & Garter
132 Water's Edge at The Greenbank Hotel
133 Rosewarne Manor Restaurant
134 Kota Restaurant with Rooms
135 Rick Stein, Porthleven
136 Victoria Inn at Perranuthnoe

137 Ben's Cornish Kitchen
138 Alba Restaurant
139 Porthminster Beach Cafe
140 The Bay at Hotel Penzance
141 Harris's Restaurant
142 The Shore Restaurant
143 Star Castle Hotel
144 The Springer Spaniel
145 The Ship Inn
146 St Moritz Hotel
147 Treglos Hotel Restaurant & Spa
148 Fistral Beach Hotel and Spa
149 Trevalsa Court
150 Bustopher Jones
151 The Watch House
152 Rick Stein's Fish
153 Rastella at Merchants Manor
154 Meudon Hotel
155 The Bay Hotel
156 The Square at Porthleven
157 Amélies
158 Porthgwidden Beach Cafe
159 Porthminster Kitchen
160 Porthmeor Cafe
161 2 Fore Street Restaurant

113
114
115
Tintagel

Launceston
144

118
119
120

147

A39

Port Isaac

146

A388

117 116

110

Padstow

Wadebridge

Callington

121

A39

145 A389

A30

122

Bodmin

Liskeard

A388

123

148 Newquay

A30

A390

A38

A392

St Austell

112 111

A3075

150

Fowey

Looe

124

A390

St Agnes

TRURO

Mevagissey

158
159
160
138
139

126

149

133

A30

A39

Camborne

125

140
141
142

St Ives
Hayle

Falmouth

127

A30

154 130

Penzance

136

A394

131

128

137

Porthleven

132

129

151

161

134
135

155 152

Coverack

153

156
157

ISLES OF SCILLY

143

St Mary's

Locations are approximate.

110

LANGMANS RESTAURANT

Culinary thrills in Callington

You don't retain two AA rosettes for over 17 years without being a bit picky. Not only does chef patron Anton Buttery source phenomenally fresh seasonal ingredients, he personally vets every supplier. Such dedication to the culinary arts (and sustainability) is special.

Wife Gail runs front of house: you're guaranteed the friendliest of welcomes before joining other guests for pre-dinner drinks. Then it's on to the formal dining room where exploring the delicate flavour combinations on each meticulously constructed tasting menu is a delicious all-evening affair.

Chef **Anton Buttery**
7 course evening tasting menu **£47.50**
Seats **24**

3 Church Street, Callington,
Cornwall, PL17 7RE
01579 384933

www.langmansrestaurant.co.uk

f Langmans Restaurant
🐦 @langmansdining

111 Ⓢ

TALLAND BAY HOTEL

Award winning Cornish cuisine

Having secured the title of Best Restaurant 2017 at the Taste of the West Awards, the team behind the culinary conquests at Talland Bay Hotel are aiming for another fruitful year.

A third AA rosette is on the agenda for head chef Nick Hawke and, judging by the skill and style displayed in his decadent dishes, the accomplished chef might just pull it off.

Fish and seafood feature throughout the à la carte offering. It's fitting, as the boutique hotel enjoys fabulous views over the coastline and sits snugly between the harbour towns of Looe and Polperro on the South West Coast Path.

Chef **Nick Hawke**
3 course lunch from **£28**
3 course dinner from **£48**
Seats **40**
Bedrooms **23**
Room rate from **£160**

Porthallow, Looe, Cornwall, PL13 2JB
01503 272667

www.tallandbayhotel.co.uk

f Talland Bay Hotel
🐦 @tallandbayhotel
📷 @tallandbayhotel

112 ⑤

THE OLD QUAY HOUSE HOTEL & RESTAURANT

Harbour views and culinary thrills

Champagne, seafood and striking views over the water are a few of the spoils at this harbourside restaurant and hotel. Other Old Quay House delights include cocktails on the terrace, gloriously grown-up suppers and lazy mornings in one of its 13 smart bedrooms.

In the heart of Fowey's bustling Fore Street, the townhouse-turned-hotel is a sanctuary for foodies seeking a local lunch, luxurious cream tea or an intimate dinner destination. Toast the evening with a glass of something special before indulging in carefully prepared seafood, locally-reared meats and vegetarian dishes.

Chef **Richard Massey**
3 course lunch from **£32**
3 course dinner from **£40**
Seats **30**
Bedrooms **13**
Room rate from **£195**

28 Fore Street, Fowey, Cornwall, PL23 1AQ
01726 833302

www.theoldquayhouse.com

f The Old Quay House Hotel
🐦 @theoldquayhouse
📷 @oldquayhouse

113 ⑤

THE PORT GAVERNE HOTEL

Idyllic coastal retreat

With whitewashed cottages, winding country lanes and a secluded cove, the 14th century fishing village of Port Gaverne is a find on the north Cornish coastline. And its namesake restaurant and hotel is another treasure worth adding to your little black book.

Head chef James Lean, formerly of Restaurant Nathan Outlaw, curates a multi-award winning menu which champions coastal, seasonal and no-ego cooking. Seafood specials pay homage to local fishermen, while sister cafe Pilchards on the Beach offers a daily menu of world flavours.

In summer, grab a sunny spot in the beer garden and tuck into Port Isaac crab sandwiches.

Photo: David Griffen

Chef **James Lean**
3 course lunch **£19**
3 course dinner from **£30**
Seats **100**
Bedrooms **15**
Room rate from **£150**

Port Gaverne, Port Isaac, Cornwall, PL29 3SQ
01208 880244

www.portgavernehotel.co.uk

f Port Gaverne Hotel
🐦 @portgaverne
📷 @port_gaverne_hotel

RESTAURANT NATHAN OUTLAW

Cornwall's culinary crown jewel

If retaining its two Michelin stars wasn't enough, Nathan Outlaw's flagship dining spot was also named the UK's Best Restaurant in this year's *The Good Food Guide*.

The accomplished chef's penchant for piscatorial plates and use of only the finest fish landed on Cornish shores warrants the restaurant's lofty position. Front of house standards are similarly high – although the team keep the experience relaxed and friendly.

To savour Nathan's spectacular seafood tasting menu at lunch or dinner, choose the downstairs bar with a front row view of all the action in the kitchen, or head to the upstairs dining room with its panorama over Port Isaac.

Chef **Nathan Outlaw**
Tasting menu **£130**
Seats **26**

6 New Road, Port Isaac, Cornwall, PL29 3SB
01208 880896

www.nathan-outlaw.com

f Restaurant Nathan Outlaw
🐦 @resnathanoutlaw
📷 @resnathanoutlaw

OUTLAW'S FISH KITCHEN

Rustic Cornish cooking

Nathan Outlaw's love affair with the Cornish catch continues at his second restaurant in Port Isaac, this one housed in a 15th century fisherman's cottage on the seafront.

Head chef Tim Barnes captains the ship here, crafting small plates of pristine seafood, and Cornish veg freshly plucked from the fields. Graze on dishes of monkfish ceviche, crispy ling and breaded plaice with something from the carefully curated drinks list.

Don't return in search of the dishes you loved on your last visit: Tim's menu changes almost daily depending on the fishermen's haul.

Chef **Tim Barnes**
Lunch plates from **£9**
Dinner plates from **£9**
Seats **24**

1 Middle Street, Port Isaac, Cornwall, PL29 3RH
01208 881183

www.nathan-outlaw.com

f Outlaw's Fish Kitchen
🐦 @fish_kitchen
📷 @fishkitchen

116 Ⓢ
ST ENODOC HOTEL
Delicious Rock retreat

Head chef (and ex *MasterChef* winner) James Nathan's cooking may be somewhat hidden away at the end of a long drive at St Enodoc Hotel, but don't let that put you off if you're a non-resident: his cooking is definitely worth a trip up the hill.

Top-notch ingredients are given the freedom to shine in all their simple beauty by this accomplished chef who understands the meaning of "less is more" (style, *not* portion).

In summer, take a seat on the terrace and dine with views of the oyster beds in the estuary. In winter, enjoy the cosy candlelit setting of the modern British interior, friendly service and, if you're lucky, a night at the beach-chic hotel.

Chef **James Nathan**
3 course lunch from **£27.50**
3 course dinner from **£37.50**
Seats **60**
Bedrooms **20**
Room rate from **£180**

Rock, near Wadebridge, Cornwall, PL27 6LA
01208 863394
www.enodoc-hotel.co.uk

f St Enodoc Hotel & Restaurant
🐦 @stenodochotel
📷 @stenodoc

117
THE MARINERS PUBLIC HOUSE
Cornish collaboration

For a casual take on the Nathan Outlaw experience (and a considerably shorter waiting list for a table) make tracks to The Mariners – Nathan's collaboration with local brewery Sharp's.

On sunny days, there are few better places to sip beer in the Cornish haze than on the dining pub's spacious balcony. Add a phenomenally fresh seafood platter to the mix and a quick drink can soon escalate to a long 'n' lazy afternoon.

Specials such as whole fish and intriguing meat cuts are often cooked over open flame, while the à la carte is pleasingly simple. Make sure to ask staff for the best pairing from the impressive craft beer and ale bill.

Chef **Zack Hawke**
3 course lunch from **£30**
3 course dinner from **£30**
Seats **60**

Rock Road, Rock, Cornwall, PL27 6LD
01208 863679
www.nathan-outlaw.com

f The Mariners Public House, Rock
🐦 @themarinersrock
📷 @themarinersrock

118 Ⓢ

THE SEAFOOD RESTAURANT

Cornish institution

This famously fishy emporium, the first in Rick and Jill Stein's portfolio of contemporary dining establishments, has attracted gourmets from across the world for three decades.

With their appetites whetted by Rick's many books and TV programmes, piscatorial pilgrims head to Padstow to sample head chef Stephane Delourme's polished execution of the author's pan global recipes.

The seafood bar at the heart of the action fascinates fish fans who enjoy watching chefs shucking oysters and preparing recently caught sashimi – plus it's a great spot to sip an aperitif and trawl a menu based around the daily catch.

Chef **Stephane Delourme**
3 course lunch from **£41**
3 course dinner from **£41**
Seats **130**
Bedrooms **16**
(and an additional 6 in St Edmund's House)
Room rate from **£165**

Riverside, Padstow, Cornwall, PL28 8BY
01841 532700
www.rickstein.com

f Rick Stein and Jill Stein - The Seafood Restaurant
🐦 @theseafood
📷 @ricksteinrestaurants

119 Ⓢ

ST PETROC'S BISTRO

Chic Padstow getaway

Hidden away from the hustle and bustle of Padstow's holidaying hordes, Rick and Jill Stein's bistro is popular with foodies in the know.

Whether you plump for a 14oz sirloin on the bone or a 30-day dry-aged Hereford steak, something sizzling from the grill is a good call. It's all part of chef Mark O'Hagan's mission to showcase the Cornish bounty through classic bistro dishes.

Start your visit with drinks in the lounge, or pop next door for a pre-dinner cocktail at sister establishment Ruby's Bar. Then feast alfresco in the pretty garden or relaxed bistro.

There's also a beautiful private dining room, designed by Jill and Kate Stein, which is ideal for a family celebration.

Chef **Mark O'Hagan**
3 course lunch from **£19.95**
3 course dinner from **£31**
Seats **50**
Bedrooms **10** (and an additional 4 in Prospect House)
Room rate from **£165**

4 New Street, Padstow, Cornwall, PL28 8EA
01841 532700
www.rickstein.com

f St Petroc's Bistro
🐦 @theseafood
📷 @ricksteinrestaurants

120 [S]

RICK STEIN'S CAFE

Globally-inspired seafood

Stein's signatory seafood dishes make this charming coastal cafe a popular choice with visitors to Padstow – as well as the locals.

Weatherboard walls, vibrant colours and wooden decor may represent contemporary Cornish style, but the food is fashioned with exotic flavours from around the globe.

Inspiration comes from south-east Asia, north Africa, India and the Mediterranean, and can be found in dishes such as whole deep fried seabass with chilli sauce, and Mount's Bay sardines with sea salt and lime.

Visit for breakfast, morning pastries, a light lunch or a sumptuous seafood dinner.

Chef **Ashley Rabey**
3 course lunch from **£21.85**
3 course dinner from **£23.50**
Seats **36**
Bedrooms **3**
Room rate from **£113**

Middle Street, Padstow, Cornwall, PL28 8AP
01841 532700

www.rickstein.com

f Rick Stein's Cafe
🐦 @theseafood
📷 @ricksteinrestaurants

121

THE CORNISH ARMS

British pub classics with Stein flair

It's the kind of cracking Cornish pub you hope to discover after a fun day at the beach – and the fact that it has Rick and Jill Stein's name on it guarantees that style and sustenance are covered.

A simple British pub menu based on Rick's recipes caters for everyone from hungry surfers to mini foodies. From Sunday roasts and world curries to steaming bowls of mussels and proper beef burgers, everything is fresh, hearty and crafted with flair.

A large outdoor eating area is ideal for kids (and dogs) who need to let off steam.

Chef **Julian Pickup**
3 course lunch from **£24**
3 course dinner from **£24**
Seats **100**

Churchtown, St Merryn, Cornwall, PL28 8ND
01841 532700

www.rickstein.com

f Cornish Arms
🐦 @thecornisharms
📷 @ricksteinrestaurants

APPLETON'S BAR & RESTAURANT

Cross-continent feasting

Cornish cookery meets Italian gastronomy at Andy Appleton's first solo venture. The former Fifteen Cornwall head chef continues to synthesise local produce with Italian inspiration, playing with flavours and sourcing ingredients from afar. Creative combinations along the lines of lobster tortellini with plankton pasta dough, and prosecco-battered polenta chips feature on a menu which changes daily.

Occupying a contemporary space above Trevibban Mill, Appleton's curates an intriguing Cornish/Italian bar and Italian wine list alongside the vineyard's own offering. Open for lunch and dinner during the week, the venue's chilled out brunch dishes channel LA cafe culture vibes on Sundays.

Photo: David Griffen

Chef **Andy Appleton**
3 course lunch from **£30**
3 course dinner from **£30**
Seats **50-100**

Trevibban Mill Vineyard & Orchards,
Dark Lane, near Padstow, Cornwall, PL27 7SE
01841 541355

www.appletonsatthevineyard.com

f Appleton's Bar & Restaurant
🐦 @_appletons
📷 @_appletons

JAMIE OLIVER'S FIFTEEN CORNWALL

Italian vibes by the sea

Jamie Oliver's Fifteen Cornwall is enjoying a little reinvigoration as a result of the arrival of new head chef, Adam Banks.

While still championing innovative, seasonal dishes rooted in Italian cuisine, Banks has brought fabulous finesse to the food.

Simple, Mediterranean-style dishes are crafted with beautifully fresh produce, and complement the stunning beachside setting with views across Watergate Bay.

It's open throughout the day, so start with breakfast then hang around with a decent coffee until lunch, or visit for a contemporary supper with creative cocktails and an interesting wine list. All profits go to the Cornwall Food Foundation.

Chef **Adam Banks**
3 course lunch from **£28**
3 course dinner from **£48**
Seats **120**

On the beach, Watergate Bay,
Cornwall, TR8 4AA
01637 861000

www.fifteencornwall.co.uk

f Fifteen Cornwall
🐦 @fifteencornwall
📷 @fifteencornwall

124
TABB'S RESTAURANT
Cornish dining institution

Portreath's loss was Truro's gain when Tabb's relocated to the city more than 12 years ago. Since then this hidden-away restaurant has become a foodie institution in the Cornish capital and garnered a loyal following of fans.

The quiet side street setting does little to herald the calibre of cooking you'll discover inside this welcoming and relaxed restaurant. High-back leather chairs, slate floors and fine crockery create a simple backdrop to Nigel Tabb's meticulously crafted two AA rosette dishes. Everything from the freshly baked bread to the homemade chocolates are crafted by the man himself as a result of cherished relationships with a network of trusty local suppliers.

Chef **Nigel Tabb**
3 course lunch from **£25**
3 course dinner from **£25**
Seats **28**

85 Kenwyn Street, Truro, Cornwall, TR1 3BZ
01872 262110

www.tabbs.co.uk

f Tabb's Restaurant
🐦 @nigeltabb

125 Ⓢ
THE LUGGER
Coastal spoils near Truro

For a dose of rustic Cornish charm – with a few contemporary luxuries thrown in – few hotels rival The Lugger's location on the rugged Roseland Peninsula.

While the facade of the 17th century smugglers' inn remains almost unchanged, the 24 coastal-chic bedrooms and smart dining space have received a thoroughly modern remodelling.

Head chef James Brougham and team specialise in lip-smackingly fresh seafood: push the boat out with locally landed lobster or delicate Cornish crab while feasting on those to-die-for views from your table.

Chef **James Brougham**
3 course lunch from **£25**
3 course dinner from **£37.50**
Seats **50**
Bedrooms **24**
Room rate from **£165**

Portloe, Truro, Cornwall, TR2 5RD
01872 501322

www.luggerhotel.co.uk

f The Lugger Portloe
🐦 @theluggerhotel

126 ⓢ
THE NARE HOTEL
Classic seaside glamour

Landscaped gardens and panoramic sea views over Carne Beach make this one of Cornwall's most charming destinations. Partake in the magic by quaffing a champagne cocktail in Ken's bar and dining in the yachty Quarterdeck Restaurant before retiring to an elegant bedroom – replete with sherry decanter and ice. For more formal occasions The Nare Dining Room, famed for its splendid Sunday roast, is a classic silver service affair.

In summer, seek sun on the terrace and enjoy lunch or an Admiral's afternoon tea while soaking up the views. The à la carte evening menu includes specialities such as local lobster and Cornwall-reared beef. Stay for the night and treat yourself to a day aboard the hotel's motor launch, complete with seafood picnic.

Chef **Brett Camborne-Paynter**
3 course lunch from **£25**
3 course dinner from **£40**
Seats **60**
Bedrooms **37**
Room rate from **£295**

Carne Beach, Veryan-in-Roseland, Cornwall, TR2 5PF
01872 501111

www.narehotel.co.uk

f The Nare Hotel
🐦 @thenarehotel
📷 @thenarehotel

127 ⓢ
THE ROSEVINE
Refined relaxation

A long, lazy meal with loved ones at The Rosevine feels like Sunday lunch at a friend's: one who happens to have a top chef in the kitchen and a large lawn with views over the peninsula.

The Georgian country house's relaxed atmosphere, band of friendly staff and simple beachy decor create a comforting home-from-home vibe, whether you're staying for the weekend or making a greedy pit-stop from a walk on the nearby South West Coast Path.

While lunch is a laid-back affair, chef Tim Pile's evening service takes an à la carte turn. Feast on classics such as seared wood pigeon with braised red cabbage and scotched quail's egg, or explore new dishes including grilled pollock with mussel ragout and potato bahji.

Photo: Bob Berry

Chef **Tim Pile**
3 course lunch from **£30**
3 course dinner from **£30**
Seats **40**
Bedrooms **16**
Room rate from **£97**

Portscatho, Truro, Cornwall, TR2 5EW
01872 580206

www.rosevine.co.uk

f The Rosevine
🐦 @therosevine
📷 @therosevinecornwall

128 S
THE IDLE ROCKS
Contemporary Cornish cool

**The ultimate in cool coastal elegance, Karen Richards'
beach-chic interiors create a stylish seaside vibe at
The Idle Rocks.**

Nestled into the harbourside in the charming fishing village
of St Mawes, the striking long white frontage, complete
with terrace, makes this Relais & Châteaux hotel and
restaurant a coveted destination for harbour-gazing and
tucking into sumptuous seafood.

Each plate at the multi-award winning restaurant is a
celebration of the surrounding Roseland Peninsula. Head
chef Guy Owen's creative, yet artfully simple, cooking
celebrates sustainable local harvests including rare-breed
meats and heritage veg from the Lost Gardens of Heligan.

On a winter's evening, enjoy a glass of fizz in front of an
open fire, while in summer the terrace is a cherished spot
for waterfront dining.

Chef **Guy Owen**
3 course lunch from **£35**
3 course dinner from **£58**
Seats **65**
Bedrooms **19**
Room rate from **£200**

Harbourside, St Mawes,
Cornwall, TR2 5AN
01326 270270
www.idlerocks.com

f The Idle Rocks
🐦 @theidlerocks
📷 @idlerocks

129 [A] [S]

HOTEL TRESANTON
St Mawes weekender

Lunch on the terrace at Hotel Tresanton is a luxurious affair; indulge in the likes of local Fal Oysters, hand dived scallops and a glass of crisp sauvignon in the late afternoon sun.

Head chef Paul Wadham ensures dinner in the restaurant is an equally memorable experience, fashioning relaxed Italian-inspired suppers which showcase Cornish suppliers and seasonal ingredients.

The pared-back approach is one that can be found throughout this band of townhouses-turned-coastal retreat in St Mawes. Thirty beautifully designed boutique bedrooms offer stunning sea views while subtropical gardens, a beach club and private wooden yacht provide plenty of ways to relax on this unique stretch of coastline.

Chef **Paul Wadham**
3 course lunch from **£29**
3 course dinner from **£46**
Seats **90**
Bedrooms **30**
Room rate from **£220**

27 Lower Castle Road, St Mawes,
Cornwall, TR2 5DR
01326 270055
www.tresanton.com

f Hotel Tresanton
🐦 @hoteltresanton
📷 @hoteltresanton

130 [A]

OLIVER'S
Award winning indie

An award winning line-up of Cornish producers queue to stock the kitchen of this independent restaurant in the heart of Falmouth. Yet the proudly local approach to sourcing is just one of the contributing factors to a Best Restaurant win for Oliver's at the *Food Reader Awards 2018*.

Owners Ken and Wendy Symons certainly earned the accolade – Wendy deftly takes care of the buzzy front of house while Ken crafts the food fuelling the chatter.

Seasonal ingredients guide modern menus which change daily (depending on what Chef can get his hands on) and are crafted into refined dishes served in a relaxed and unfussy setting.

Chef **Ken Symons**
3 course lunch from **£22.50**
3 course dinner from **£32**
Seats **28**

33 High Street, Falmouth, Cornwall, TR11 2AD
01326 218138
www.oliversfalmouth.com

🐦 @oliversfalmouth

STAR & GARTER

Game–changing dining pub

The Star & Garter may have perched on the banks of Falmouth harbour since 1892, but the current team running the historic pub have adopted a forward-thinking food philosophy.

Head chef Andrew Richardson and his brigade butcher, smoke and cure all of the locally reared meat that lands in the kitchen, before using almost all of the animal in a line-up of inventive nose-to-tail dishes.

Visiting on the weekend? Bag a roomy booth boasting killer views of the water, make easy work of the creative cocktail menu then stay in one of the Pinterest-worthy bedrooms. It's also worth sticking around for the Falmouth-famous Sunday roast.

Chef **Andrew Richardson**
3 course lunch from **£18**
3 course dinner from **£26**
Seats **40**
Bedrooms **4**
Room rate from **£90**

52 High Street, Falmouth, Cornwall, TR11 2AF
01326 316663

www.starandgarterfalmouth.co.uk

f Star & Garter Falmouth
🐦 @starfalmouth
📷 @starandgarterfalmouth

WATER'S EDGE AT THE GREENBANK HOTEL

Phenomenal views in Falmouth

With a knockout spot (and panoramic panes) overlooking the harbour, the Water's Edge Restaurant has one of the best backdrops on the Cornish coast.

Executive chef Nick Hodges ensures the seasonally changing menu produces similar awe. Whatever time of year you visit, you'll find a pleasing selection of seafood dishes such as potted Cornish crab alongside locally-reared meats and inspired veggie options.

Book one of The Greenbank's contemporary bedrooms and make the most of the bartender's creative concoctions in the cocktail lounge.

Chef **Nick Hodges**
3 course lunch from **£22**
3 course dinner from **£25**
Seats **80**
Bedrooms **61**
Room rate from **£109**

Harbourside, Falmouth, Cornwall, TR11 2SR
01326 312440

www.greenbank-hotel.co.uk

f The Greenbank Hotel
🐦 @greenbankhotel
📷 @greenbankhotel

Piscatorial pleasures

63 Hix Oyster & Fish House

Sit on the terrace that overlooks the magnificent Jurassic Coast as you graze your way through plates of Lyme Bay mackerel, Newlyn gurnard and Portland cock crab.

115 Outlaw's Fish Kitchen

Carefully crafted small plates of pristine seafood and freshly plucked Cornish veg delight at this Outlaw's outpost. Tim Barnes' ever-revolving piscatorial offering depends on the daily haul: look out for faves like monkfish ceviche and crispy ling.

108 Salcombe Harbour Hotel & Spa

Enjoy briny-fresh oysters, Devon crab, Salcombe Gin-cured salmon or 'Jetty on a Plate' on the terrace at this glam spa hotel. Then finish the night in a nautical-chic bedroom and slumber to the sound of the sea outside your window.

142 The Shore Restaurant

Sensational seafood suppers await at Bruce Rennie's modern bistro in Penzance. A minimal menu delights with treats that vary according to the local dayboats' catch.

56 Riverside Restaurant

The banks of the River Brit set the scene for Dorset day-trippers' fish fix at Riverside. Spend a lazy afternoon cracking shells, slurping oysters and clinking champagne flutes as you enjoy stonking views across the water.

No 112
THE OLD QUAY HOUSE
HOTEL & RESTAURANT

133

ROSEWARNE MANOR RESTAURANT

For epicurean events

Enswathed in verdant Cornish countryside, this family-run dining destination is well worth a pit-stop on your travels. Now in its eleventh year with the same head chef, it has achieved consistently high standards, holding two AA rosettes and a gold Taste of the West Award for five years.

Hearty dishes on the bar menu are usually based around Cornish ingredients while the modern British à la carte cuisine looks almost too good to eat. With three dining rooms, a well-stocked bar and large garden, Rosewarne is also a popular wedding and events venue.

Chef **Phil Thomas**
3 course lunch from **£20**
3 course dinner from **£29**
Seats **36**

Gwinear Road, Connor Downs, Hayle,
Cornwall, TR27 5JQ
01209 610414

www.rosewarnemanor.co.uk

f Rosewarne Manor Restaurant & function venue
🐦 @rosewarnemanor

134 Ⓢ

KOTA RESTAURANT WITH ROOMS

Asian fusion feasting

Jude Kereama's fusion cooking draws upon his half Maori and half Chinese heritage – with a good dose of creativity thrown in. The chef has become a familiar face on BBC Two, having twice represented the South West on *Great British Menu*.

A 300-year-old building on Porthleven's historic harbour creates an atmospheric backdrop to these sumptuous two AA rosette, Michelin Bib Gourmand dishes, providing an Asia-meets-New Zealand twist on local seafood.

Add a stonking cellar which draws on Jude and wife Jane's passion for wines from across the globe, and it's worth booking one of the two delightful B&B rooms for the night.

Chef **Jude Kereama**
3 course dinner from **£27**
Seats **30**
Bedrooms **2**
Room rate from **£85**

Harbour Head, Porthleven,
Cornwall, TR13 9JA
01326 562407

www.kotarestaurant.co.uk

f Kota
🐦 @kotarestaurant

RICK STEIN, PORTHLEVEN

Inspired by Rick's travels

Jill Stein's seaside-chic decor is a taste of Cornish cool at this Porthleven favourite. Whitewashed walls, bare wooden boards and sea-bright metal chairs all contribute to its stylishly relaxed vibe.

Sharing platters of globally-inspired cuisine and creative specialities based on the daily catch prove a hit with diners, while dishes inspired by Rick's travels around the world – such as Singapore chilli crab or Goan cod curry – put an exotic twist on local, seasonal produce.

By day, it's home to light seafood snacks, well priced set menus and dishes suited to a long leisurely lunch with a glass or two of wine. By night, the restaurant offers intimate cosy feasting.

Chef **Ashley Gains**
3 course lunch from **£21.50**
3 course dinner from **£26**
Seats **75**

Mount Pleasant, Porthleven, Cornwall, TR13 9JS
01326 565636

www.rickstein.com

f   Rick Stein, Porthleven
🐦 @steinporthleven
📷 @ricksteinrestaurants

VICTORIA INN AT PERRANUTHNOE

The locals' choice

The Victoria Inn is the kind of pub we all dream of stumbling across when traversing Cornwall's warren of country lanes.

If you do happen upon it, you'll find a strong wine list and a bar brimming with regional ales, alongside an impressive menu of contemporary classics – not to mention two cosy bedrooms so you won't have to hit the road again until morning.

Chef patron Nik Boyle's modern-dining take on traditional pub food makes the 16th century inn popular with both locals and visiting ramblers. Expect slick service too: the team scooped the Trencherman's Best Front of House award in 2017.

Chef **Nik Boyle**
3 course lunch from **£17.50**
3 course dinner from **£24**
Seats **40**
Bedrooms **2**
Room rate from **£95**

Church Town Road, Perranuthnoe, Penzance, Cornwall, TR20 9NP
01736 710309

www.victoriainn-penzance.co.uk

f   Victoria Inn at Perranuthnoe
📷 @therealvictoriainn

137 Ⓐ

BEN'S CORNISH KITCHEN

Fine wining and dining

While many make the pilgrimage to Marazion to sample Ben Prior's modern Cornish cooking, gastronomes in the know also flock to this 2016 Trencherman's Best Restaurant for the chef patron's fabulous wine pairings.

Each dish on Ben's daily-updated menu is matched with a pick from his cellar, which is available by the glass or carafe. A modest offering of three or four dishes at each course enables the chef to keep the experience hyper-local and pleasingly personal.

It's one of the few Cornish indies to remain open all year, so visit in low season to make the most of the local winter veg and quiet coastline.

Chef **Ben Prior**
3 course lunch from **£24**
3 course dinner from **£35**
Seats **32**

Marazion, Penzance, Cornwall, TR17 0EL
01736 719200
www.benscornishkitchen.com

f Ben's Cornish Kitchen
🐦 @cornishkitchen

138 Ⓐ

ALBA RESTAURANT

Smart supping in surfy St Ives

An evening at this lifeboat station-turned-harbourside dining hangout should be started with a pre-dinner cocktail. After all, Alba's sleek ground floor bar was named as one of the best in the South West at the Trencherman's Awards 2018.

Once installed at a table in the glass-panelled dining room, award winning pleasures come in the form of chef patron Grant Nethercott's modern British menus. There's a stunningly good selection of fish and seafood – locally sourced, naturally – which is simply enhanced with Cornish and foraged ingredients and herbs from Grant's garden.

Chef **Grant Nethercott**
3 course dinner from **£35**
Seats **36**

Old Lifeboat House, Wharf Road, St Ives, Cornwall, TR26 1LF
01736 797222
www.alba-stives.co.uk

f Alba Restaurant and Bar St.Ives
🐦 @albarestaurant
📷 @albarestaurantstives

CORNWALL 131

139

PORTHMINSTER BEACH CAFE

Seafood and sea views

Bountiful seafood platters and beautiful sea views are the bewitching prospect at this beach cafe which shimmers on sands beneath Porthminster cliffs.

The vista over St Ives Bay makes this an idyllic spot in which to indulge in the local catch. Many of the accompanying veggies, herbs and salads are picked from the cafe's garden or foraged from nearby coastal paths, ensuring Porthminster lives up to its ethos of sourcing everything as locally as possible.

The warm terrace makes a fabulous backdrop to the Mediterranean and Asian-inspired dishes, while evening views over the ocean are sublime.

Chef **Mick Smith**
3 course lunch from **£30**
3 course dinner from **£40**
Seats **80**

Porthminster Beach, St Ives, Cornwall, TR26 2EB
01736 795352

www.porthminstercafe.co.uk

f Porthminster Cafe
🐦 @porthbcafe
📷 @porthminstercafe

140 Ⓢ

THE BAY AT HOTEL PENZANCE

Bird's eye brasserie

The sweeping views across Mount's Bay and impressive cooking from head chef Ben Reeve make for a dinner of distinction at The Bay. And the fact that Ben has retained two AA rosettes here for 12 years demonstrates his culinary commitment and passion.

The current menu of modern dishes is described as 'best of British with a nod to France', featuring classics such as côte de boeuf, West Country mussels and an impressive cheese selection. Sip an aperitif at sunset on the terrace before getting to grips with a locally landed lobster. Then toddle off to one of the 25 comfy guest rooms at this townhouse hotel.

Chef **Ben Reeve**
3 course lunch from **£20**
3 course dinner from **£32**
Seats **50**
Bedrooms **25**
Room rate from **£90**

Britons Hill, Penzance, Cornwall, TR18 3AE
01736 366890

www.thebaypenzance.co.uk

f The Bay Restaurant
🐦 @perfectpenzance

141
HARRIS'S RESTAURANT
Local legend

In the capable hands of the Harris family for over three decades, this Penzance restaurant has long enjoyed a following of both locals and visiting foodies.

A pleasing line-up of classic dishes crafted from fish landed at Newlyn, Cornish meats and locally-grown vegetables keep them coming back for chef Roger Harris's food. Menus change almost daily but diners are often treated to delights such as whole Cornish lobster, grilled fillet steak and loin of venison.

Start the evening with something special from the carefully curated wine list in the bar before moving on to dinner in the refined restaurant.

Chef **Roger Harris**
3 course lunch from **£27.50**
3 course dinner from **£27.50**
Seats **20** restaurant, **20** bar

46 New Street, Penzance, Cornwall, TR18 2LZ
01736 364408
www.harrissrestaurant.co.uk

142
THE SHORE RESTAURANT
Sensational seafood suppers

This modest modern bistro houses one of the country's finest fish restaurants. Chef patron Bruce Rennie previously captained two Michelin-starred kitchens – Edinburgh's Restaurant Martin Wishart and Shanks in Northern Ireland – and launched his solo project in 2016.

The seasoned chef's skill is such that the minimal menu – just two or three seafood options for each course – makes choosing a cinch. The menu changes daily and depends on the local dayboats' haul, but the five or seven course tasting menus are the prize catch – and come with a pleasingly reasonable price tag, too.

Photo: Nick Hook Photography

Chef **Bruce Rennie**
3 course dinner from **£36**
Seats **30**

13-14 Alverton Street, Penzance, Cornwall, TR18 2QP
01736 362444
www.theshorerestaurant.uk

f The Shore Restaurant
🐦 @the_shore_pz
📷 @the_shore_pz

STAR CASTLE HOTEL
A taste of the Scilly Isles

Located in a 16th century castle with spectacular views over the archipelago, this family-run hotel is unique. And with excellent customer service and classic menus in the two award winning restaurants, it's a very civilised place to stay.

Produce doesn't get more local than the Star Castle's kitchen garden and island suppliers, while the Scillonian lobster and crab are caught by the proprietor himself. After dinner, descend to the Dungeon Bar to sip Cornish ales or wines from the house vineyard. Then retreat to one of the castle's characterful beamed guest rooms or a charming cottage-style retreat set in four acres of subtropical gardens.

Chef **Billy Littlejohn**
3 course dinner from **£42**
Seats **40**
Bedrooms **38**
Room rate from **£85**

The Garrison, St Mary's,
Isles of Scilly, TR21 0JA
01720 422317

www.star-castle.co.uk

f Star Castle Hotel
🐦 @starcastlehotel
📷 @starcastlehotel

CHEF'S TIP

Grant Nethercott, chef patron at Alba Restaurant (No 138)

'I'm keen to visit The Mariners Public House in Rock (No 117), as I haven't eaten at one of Nathan's restaurants since he got his first Michelin star at The Black Pig.'

More Cornwall

144
THE SPRINGER SPANIEL

This delightfully rustic 18th century country pub is renowned among Launceston locals for its tail-waggingly good selection of ales and freshly prepared menus, with ingredients sourced from local farms. The Springer welcomes all, so choose between a lingering meal for two from the tasting menu, a family-friendly à la carte evening or simply a casual meet-up with mates for Cornish tapas. A visit isn't complete without a tipple from the cocktail menu: try the Hugo for a prosecco, elderflower, lime and mint mash-up.

Chef **Connor Hawkings**. 3 course lunch from **£25**. 3 course dinner from **£25**. Seats **35**

Treburley, Launceston, Cornwall, PL15 9NS
01579 370424
www.thespringerspaniel.co.uk

f The Springer Spaniel
🐦 @springerthe
📷 @thespringerspanielpub

145
THE SHIP INN

Hop aboard Wadebridge's award winning Ship – one of the oldest pubs in town – to discover a haven of wholesome, well-cooked food, friendly folk and a cracking drinks line-up: don't leave without sampling a glass of Sharp's ale, Tarquin's gin or Camel Valley fizz.

Chef Craig Jeffrey, finalist in 2018's Pub Chef of the Year competition, crafts classics using locally sourced produce. Enjoy them while cosied on a leather banquette by the fire as you admire the nautical memorabilia.

Chef **Craig Jeffery**. 3 course lunch from **£19**. 3 course dinner from **£24**. Seats **70**

Gonvena Hill, Wadebridge, Cornwall, PL27 6DF
01208 813845
www.shipinnwadebridge.co.uk

f The Ship Inn - Gonvena Hill, Wadebridge
🐦 @shipinngonvena
📷 @shipinngonvena

146 S
ST MORITZ HOTEL

This stylish art deco hotel is in a superb spot for those exploring north Cornwall's sandy beaches and azure waters, as all of its beach-chic accommodation (rooms, suites or self-catering apartments and villas) is just a stroll from the shore.

Watch dinner being prepared in the open kitchen at the Shorecrest Restaurant before devouring dishes showcasing fresh-from-the-ocean seafood and Cornish bounty. Or, if you're still sandy from the beach, head to the Sea Side cafe which, from brunch to dinner, pleases all appetites with seafood platters, sharing dishes, salads and steaks.

3 course lunch from **£25**.
3 course dinner from **£30**. Seats **60**.
Bedrooms **55**. Room rate from **£120**

Trebetherick, Wadebridge, Cornwall, PL27 6SD
01208 862242
www.stmoritzhotel.co.uk

f St Moritz Hotel Cornwall
𝕏 @stmoritzhotel
◎ @stmoritzhotel

147 S
TREGLOS HOTEL RESTAURANT & SPA

Sun-seeking couples, surf-worshipping families and city folk enjoying a coastal fix swap stories at Treglos Hotel near Padstow. While surf dudes dally in Constantine Bay's undulating dunes, those averse to the sand make their way around the 18 hole golf course – avoiding the bunkers, of course – or soak away the hours in the Glo Spa. However the day is spent, guests can look forward to a decadent dinner in the hotel's Quies Restaurant. Don something smart for a drink in the bar before joining fellow guests for a feast of Cornish fare prepared by new head chef David Koeman.

Chef **David Koeman**. 3 course dinner from **£40**.
Seats **80**. Bedrooms **42**. Room rate from **£175**

Constantine Bay, Padstow, Cornwall, PL28 8JH
01841 520727
www.tregloshotel.com

f Treglos Hotel
𝕏 @tregloshotel
◎ @tregloshotel

148 S
FISTRAL BEACH HOTEL AND SPA

Whether you've spent your day bobbing in the Newquay surf, exploring the coast path or enjoying a spot of TLSea in the spa, a sensational supper awaits at Fistral Beach Hotel. Its Dune Restaurant not only harbours incredible views of the hotel's namesake beach, it also serves some of the freshest seafood caught on Cornish shores. Vibrant veggies and steaks on Lee Highcock's contemporary menu are sourced with similar vigour for quality. Leave the heels at home; relaxed interiors channel chilled-out beach vibes.

Chef **Lee Highcock**. 3 course lunch from **£25**.
3 course dinner from **£29**. Seats **150**.
Bedrooms **71**. Room rate from **£80**

Esplande Road, Newquay, Cornwall, TR7 1PT
01637 818087
www.fistralbeachhotel.co.uk

f Fistral Beach Hotel
𝕏 @fistralbeachh
◎ @fistralbeachhotel

149 S
TREVALSA COURT

For an elegant dose of 'vitamin sea', head to cliffside Trevalsa Court.

Originally a grand seaside home, its dazzling ocean views, subtropical gardens and understated sense of style give guests a revitalising taste of Cornwall.

Local flavour is also on display in the sumptuous selection of two AA rosette dishes such as monkfish with galette potatoes, shaved fennel, clams and mussel bon-bons.

Follow with games by the fire on cool days, or linger on the terrace with a glass of something crisp on balmy evenings.

Chef **Adam Cawood**. 3 course lunch from **£13.99**. 3 course dinner from **£25**.
Seats **30**. Bedrooms **14**. Room rate from **£100**

School Hill, Mevagissey, Cornwall, PL26 6TH
01726 842468
www.trevalsa-hotel.co.uk

f Trevalsa Court Hotel and Restaurant
𝕏 @trevalsacourt
◎ @trevalsacourt

150
BUSTOPHER JONES

Step inside this restored Georgian townhouse to discover an unexpected dining experience. Artistic flair runs throughout – from the elegant bar to the outdoor seating area to the weird and wonderful cocktail list with its array of homemade bitters and tinctures.

While there are plenty of quirky elements, the menus take quality ingredients seriously: chef Darren Millgate pays homage to the provenance of Cornish produce, in particular its wealth of seafood, and cooks it in style, adding touches of global inspiration.

Chef **Darren Millgate**. 3 course lunch from **£15**. 3 course dinner from **£27**. Seats **80**

62 Lemon Street, Truro, Cornwall, TR1 2PN
01872 430000
www.bustopher-jones.co.uk

f Bustopher Jones
𝕏 @bustopherjones_
◎ @bustopherjonestruro

151
THE WATCH HOUSE

This busy bistro has become a magnet for both tourists and locals.

Right on the harbour in the fishing village of St Mawes, its building used to be the Customs and Excise Watch House and a pilchard press.

Now its mission is to serve the freshest, simply cooked Cornish seafood – which it does in style. Downstairs you'll find cosy booths, while the upstairs dining room is light and airy with views across the sea to St Anthony's Head.

If you've no time to linger over lunch, grab a helping of MSC certified fish with hand cut, double-cooked chips to take away from The Watch Out hatch.

Chef **Will Gould**. 3 course lunch from **£25**. 3 course dinner from **£35**. Seats **70**

1 The Square, St Mawes, Cornwall, TR2 5DJ
01326 270038
www.watchhousestmawes.co.uk

f The Watch House
𝕏 the_watch_house
◎ @the_watchhouse_cornwall

152
RICK STEIN'S FISH

This seafood restaurant and takeaway in maritime Falmouth has a seaside classic at its heart: really good fish and chips (cooked in beef dripping for superior flavour and bite) are served alongside some of Rick's well known dishes such as Indonesian seafood curry, and salt and pepper prawns.

Swing by for a crowd-pleasing lunch with kids or book a grown-up supper with chums – walk-ins are also welcome. Quality beers and wines (there's nothing like a glass of fizz with fish and chips) kick the experience up another notch, while warm service and an unpretentious vibe have made this a popular haunt.

Chef **Dominic Gill**. 3 course lunch from **£19.95**. 3 course dinner from **£23.95**. Seats **70**

Discovery Quay, Falmouth, Cornwall, TR11 3XA
01326 330050
www.rickstein.com

f Rick Stein's Fish, Falmouth
𝕏 @steinsfalmouth
◎ @ricksteinrestaurants

153 ⓢ
RASTELLA AT MERCHANTS MANOR

It's not just the chef who gets the credit for food served in Falmouth's 100-year-old country house hotel and spa. From the forager to the organic gardener, a small team ensures diners experience genuinely local ingredients.

Dishes are seasonal with landscape themes, like the Rockpool starter of Cornish lobster, Porthilly oyster, smoked aioli and seaweed. Look out for dishes roasted in Bertha, the wood-fired oven.

Chef **Hylton Espey**. 3 course lunch from **£20**. 3 course dinner from **£30**. Seats **64**. Bedrooms **39**. Room rate from **£120**

1 Western Terrace, Falmouth, Cornwall, TR11 4QJ
0 1326 369564
www.merchantsmanor.com

f Merchants Manor
𝕏 @merchantsmanor
◎ @rastellarestaurant

154 [S]
MEUDON HOTEL

The magic of Meudon is its utterly unique setting: nine acres of subtropical gardens leading down to Bream Cove, its own idyllic private beach. Rare and exotic plants from all over the world make this wonderful Cornish valley garden worth the visit alone.

Add to that the four star hotel accommodation and rosette-worthy dishes served in the fine dining restaurant, Bream Cove, and this is a fabulous hideaway for unwinding and relaxing. Each of the bedrooms offers a touch of luxury and gorgeous views, while dinner is served against the vista of the valley garden and Falmouth Bay.

Chef **Teresena Andrewartha**. 3 course lunch from **£22.50**. 3 course dinner from **£35**. Seats **50**. Bedrooms **29**. Room rate from **£100**

Mawnan Smith, Falmouth, Cornwall, TR11 5HT
01326 250541

www.meudon.co.uk

f Meudon Hotel
🐦 @meudonhotel
📷 @meudonhotel

155 [S]
THE BAY HOTEL

In an unspoilt coastal location in the fishing village of Coverack, the stunning panoramic sea views across the beach from the private gardens of The Bay Hotel are well worth a visit. But once you've planned your sailing, swimming and surfing schedule, step inside the hotel to be treated to attentive and friendly service, delightful dining and a selection of Cornish gins, beers and wines. The daily-changing menu is a sumptuous display of the local larder, and don't miss the speciality: lobsters landed straight from the bay.

Chef **Chris Conboye**. 3 course lunch from **£21.95**. 3 course dinner from **£35**. Seats **36**. Bedrooms **14**. Room rate from **£190**

Coverack, near Helston, Cornwall, TR12 6TF
01326 280464

www.thebayhotel.co.uk

f The Bay Hotel Coverack
🐦 @bayhotelc

156
THE SQUARE AT PORTHLEVEN

Life is good when you're sitting on the sunny terrace of this Michelin Bib restaurant, savouring succulent seafood and taking in the sweep of Porthleven's harbour. The lunchtime menu centres around well-crafted classics such as fish and chips, BLTs and charcuterie platters. Come evening, a sumptuous dinner menu includes treats such as slow-cooked Cornish pork belly with black pudding and crispy polenta.

Stock up on cheeses and charcuterie from the adjoining Deli and Ice Cream Emporium – and don't miss out on a cone of owners Anna and Stewart Eddy's handmade ices.

Chef **Bryok Williams**. 3 course lunch from **£22.50**. 3 course dinner from **£24.50**. Seats **36**

7 Fore Street, Porthleven, Cornwall, TR13 9HQ
01326 573911

www.thesquareatporthleven.co.uk

f The Square at Porthleven
🐦 @thesquarepl
📷 @thesquarepl

157
AMÉLIES

Sitting pretty on Porthleven's picturesque harbour, this rustic chic, family-friendly restaurant outperforms its promise of 'simple food, perfectly cooked with soul'.

Visit for super-fresh Cornish seafood dishes and wood-fired pizzas – and if you visit on a Sunday lunchtime you can pair it with live music played on the baby grand.

A new oak and glass terrace, with panoramic harbour views, creates a brilliant venue for weddings and parties. High ceilings, sparkly sails and designer driftwood tables make this a romantic spot for all occasions.

Chef **Donato Dondiego**. 3 course lunch from **£20**. 3 course dinner from **£20**. Seats **93**

Breageside, Porthleven, Cornwall, TR13 9JS
01326 653653

www.ameliesporthleven.co.uk

f Amélies, Porthleven
🐦 @amelies_kernow
📷 @ameliesporthleven

158
PORTHGWIDDEN BEACH CAFE

This friendly all-day cafe sits on the sands of St Ives and offers alfresco dining right on the beach, as well as scenic views across the bay to Godrevy Lighthouse. As a result it's a popular venue for weddings, although for informal days chalets are available for beach addicts.

The cooking mostly centres on local Cornish seafood (from St Ives, Looe and Mevagissey) which is given contemporary Mediterranean and Asian tweaks. Expect unfussy, hearty dishes that are perfect for satisfying that salty sea-air hunger – even if you're just lolling about in the sun.

Chef **Robert Michael**. 3 course lunch from **£25**. 3 course dinner from **£35**. Seats **50**

The Island, St Ives, Cornwall, TR26 1PL
01736 796791
www.porthgwiddencafe.co.uk

f Porthgwidden Beach Cafe
🐦 @pgwidden

159
PORTHMINSTER KITCHEN

Younger and buzzier than its iconic sibling (Porthminster Beach Cafe), the Kitchen offers gull's eye, panoramic views over the bustling St Ives harbour, either through the huge picture windows or from the sun-drenched terrace.

You'll find a relaxed, global approach to the Cornish catch, as found in the PK Seafood Curry of local fish, mussels, prawns, bok choy and sweet potato.

Dairy and gluten take an on-trend back seat in favour of small plates and lighter options, while Sunday roasts have had a memorable modern makeover.

Chef **Paul Oliver**. 3 course lunch from **£30**. 3 course dinner from **£35**. Seats **48**

Wharf Road, St Ives, Cornwall, TR26 1LG
01736 799874
www.porthminster.kitchen

f Porthminster Kitchen
🐦 @pkitchenstives
📷 @porthminster_kitchen

160
PORTHMEOR CAFE

This buzzy beachside cafe is open from breakfast through to dinner. Gear up for the day with a locally roasted Origin coffee, signed with impressive latte art by the baristas; follow with modern Med-style tapas dishes based around what's fresh and local; or sip a cocktail with a twist on the terrace and keep an eye out for the occasional offshore dolphin.

Enjoy the panoramic views from inside too, or cosy up for alfresco dining (try the crispy fried seabass, chilli caramel and pineapple Asian salad) in one of the cute heated pods.

Chefs **Cameron Jennings & Louis Wardman**. 3 course lunch from **£18**. 3 course dinner from **£25**. Seats **30** inside, **30** on each terrace

Porthmeor, St Ives, Cornwall, TR26 1JZ
01736 793366
www.porthmeor-beach.co.uk

f Porthmeor Beach, Cafe Bar and Surf School, St Ives
📷 @porthmeorcafe

161
2 FORE STREET RESTAURANT

Whether it's lunch straight after a beach trip or a sumptuous three course dinner cooked by classically trained chef Joe Wardell, the appeal of this relaxed and stylish eatery is no big mystery.

Set on Mousehole harbour, its views across the fishing village and Mount's Bay are stunning, while the lively continental vibe appeals to holidaymakers and locals alike.

Joe refreshes the menu regularly to reflect the area's best seafood and organic meat. And on long summer days, a secluded garden is the coveted spot for alfresco eating.

Chef **Joe Wardell**. 3 course lunch from **£27**. 3 course dinner from **£32**. Seats **36**

Mousehole, Penzance, Cornwall, TR19 6PF
01736 731164
www.2forestreet.co.uk

Wine notes

For details of those special wines you've experienced at
Trencherman's restaurants

Wine notes

For details of those special wines you've experienced at
Trencherman's restaurants

Index

TRENCHERMAN'S
GUIDE

EDITION

26